The Essence of
DARWINISM

THE MODERN BELIEFS SERIES

Kirsten Birkett

MATTHIAS MEDIA

The Essence of Darwinism
© Matthias Media, 2001

Matthias Media
PO Box 225, Kingsford NSW 2032, Australia
Telephone: (02) 9663 1478   Facsimile: (02) 9663 3265
International: +61-2-9663 1478   Facsimile: +61-2-9663 3265
Email: info@matthiasmedia.com.au
Internet: www.matthiasmedia.com.au

Distributed in South Africa by:
Christian Book Discounters
ph (021) 685 3663
email: peter@christianbooks.co.za

Distributed in the United Kingdom by:
The Good Book Company
ph (020) 8942 0880
email: admin@thegoodbook.co.uk

ISBN 1 876326 39 5

Cover design and typesetting by Joy Lankshear Design Pty Ltd.
Printed in Australia.

Contents

Preface

THE MODERN BELIEFS SERIES

The world is shaped by what we believe: our values, our society, our daily activities will reflect what we believe to be true and important. This is the case for everyone, not just those who consider themselves 'religious' or 'having faith'. Whatever beliefs a person may hold, be they secular, atheist, religious, modern, traditional, scientific, artistic or a mixture of them all, that person's world view and way of life will reflect their underlying ideological conviction.

Most people go through life happily (or unhappily) unaware of their beliefs. It's easy to assume that what we think is what everyone does, or just never think about it at all. It's a sad way to be, both for individuals and for the society we create. If Socrates considered "the unexamined life is not worth living", we might add "the unexamined society is not worth having"— if we don't understand what we believe and why society is the way it is, we will never be able to affect it for the better.

The 'Modern Beliefs' series is not meant to be the final word on everything. It is meant to describe the essence of the beliefs that pervade our world; the ideas that tell us who we are, why we are here and what we ought to do about it. There are many such ideas, most of them inherited from past ages, some newly invented. We have no particular criteria for what comes under the heading 'Modern Beliefs'; if it has affected our culture today, it's worth understanding.

Our world is full of so many ideas it can be confusing just waking up in the morning. We hope that the 'Modern Beliefs' series will help to make at least a few parts of it more understandable.

About *The Essence of Darwinism*

A beautifully simple and easily understood idea—evolution by natural selection—can be scientifically tested in [many scientific] fields. It is one of the most powerful ideas in all science, and is the only theory that can seriously claim to unify biology. It can give meaning to facts from the invisible world found in a drop of rainwater, or from the many coloured delights of a botanic garden, or thundering herds of big game. The theory is also used to understand such topics as the geochemistry of life's origins and the gaseous proportions of the modern atmosphere. As Theodosius Dobzhansky, one of the twentieth century's most eminent evolutionary biologists, remarked in an often quoted but scarcely exaggerated phrase, "nothing in biology makes sense except in the light of evolution".[1]

This fervent praise of evolutionary theory, fairly moderate as such praises go, appears in the first chapter of a standard textbook of evolutionary biology. Students are to understand that in studying evolution by natural selection, they are approaching one of the most magnificent efforts of human endeavour in understanding the world. Praise frequently goes beyond that, in textbooks and popular works on evolutionary biology; we are frequently told that evolution is a fact, that it is the greatest story of mankind, that we are fools if we don't believe it, and so on.

The subtext of such statements is not hard to find.

1. Mark Ridley, *Evolution*, Blackwell Science, Oxford, 1996.

Evolutionary theory receives such high praise from its adherents in opposition to certain religious groups—'fundamentalists', considered to be a derogatory term—who do not think evolution is true. Indeed, many scientific texts take the time to address specifically religious objections to evolution.

Now it is not unusual for any given scientific theory to be disputed and defended. What is unusual about evolutionary theory is that it is disputed and defended with such heartfelt fervour—geologist Ian Plimer even sold his house to prosecute 'creation scientists' for false advertising. No discussion of evolutionary theory, even in an innocuous introductory textbook, is without echoes of religious fervour of some kind. Evolutionary science is not just a study of the history of life. It is a theological—or anti-theological—weapon.

What I wish to understand is: why is there no end to the fierce religious battles over Darwinism?

I have tried to achieve four simple goals in this book. The first goal is to explain (in Part I) what the modern theory is to non-biologists, and how the theory has changed since Darwin's time—to the extent that to call the modern theory 'Darwinism' is almost a misnomer. I have tried also, in Part II, to demonstrate where the points of tension are within the evolutionary science community itself. This discussion contains fairly dense scientific argument, which the reader may skip if not interested in such details. Part III looks at the history of conflict between Darwinism and religion, and Part IV tries to make sense of this conflict, heading towards a resolution.

I have had some qualms about calling this book 'The Essence of Darwinism'. Given my wish, I would call it 'Introductory thoughts towards an initial exploration of Darwinism', or something similarly humble. However publishing forces beyond my control (i.e. my senior editor) consider the book a fitting candidate for the 'Essence of' series, so the title stands. Nonetheless, more remains to be explored in the philosophy of evolution and its connections with religion.

I *have* tried to isolate the fundamental motivation for the angst generated by Darwinism. What I wish to demonstrate is that evolution is not, and never has been, simply a scientific theory. It is a theory which has always been connected to fervent religious (usually anti-Christian) beliefs, and has frequently been held and defended by members of the scientific community purely because of their religious convictions, not because of its scientific value.

This in itself does not prove evolutionary theory untrue. It does, however, suggest that we are taking the wrong tack by discussing whether the theory is scientifically valid or not. We need to take more seriously the fact that this theory is not about science, but about how we understand humanity. If people are uptight about evolution, it is not because they are (or are not) scientific. It is because there are things to explain about being human in our world which matter. I hope this books serves to clarify some of these things and what we should do about them.

There is no bibliography of books on evolutionary theory, for that would probably be a book in itself. I have given specific footnotes concerning individuals or ideas mentioned, for those who wish to follow them up. I make no distinction between 'religious' and 'secular' books: it is part of my argument that no book about evolution will be theologically neutral. That is something the reader must understand in researching evolution.

I would like to thank my colleagues at Matthias Media for

their patient ears as I have researched this material, and Tony Payne in particular for his editing suggestions. Professor Peter Barry (School of Physiology and Pharmacology, UNSW), Dr Ian McFarlane (School of Biochemistry, UNSW) and Dr Shane Ahyong (The Australian Museum) read the parts of the book explaining scientific ideas and I thank them for their comments. I also thank my friends in the Postgraduate Bible Fellowship for the many conversations, as well as formal feedback, I enjoyed from that group. Knowledge is a continual process and I no doubt have much left to learn.

Kirsten Birkett
SYDNEY, 2001

Part I

DARWINIAN EVOLUTION: WHAT IS IT?

What is evolutionary theory? In one sense this question is impossible to answer because it is hopelessly vague. It is rather like asking 'what is geological theory?'. In geology there are *thousands* of theories, depending on what part of the earth is being studied and what is interesting about it. Any particular geologist will have a research problem to work on, with ideas about the solution to that problem. Colleagues may agree or disagree with these theories or have theories of their own. To ask, simply, 'What is geological theory?' is to misunderstand what is being done.

In evolutionary science, too, there are thousands of theories just as there are many different areas being studied. Scientists concerned with evolution may be population geneticists or ecologists or animal behaviourists or molecular biologists. They may be concerned with classifying plants or digging up fossils or studying rainforests; their objects of study can be arthropods or antelopes or the Amazon. It is a vast area with thousands of specific fields to work on, each with their own particular problems. How much does genetic variation in a colony of fruit-flies change after ten generations? What is the genome of a worm? What mathematical structure captures the way in which theoretical populations change over time? To talk of one 'evolutionary theory' or of 'evolution' as an area of study, is to vastly oversimplify a huge range of activity and ideas.

However oversimplifications seem to be stock-in-trade for evolution and its political battles. When legal debates rage over whether evolution can be taught in schools, or magazines run articles on the latest controversy, what is described as 'evolution' by the various bodies involved can be vastly different from the specialized, highly technical and sophisticated studies actually being done. Practising scientists understandably react with some annoyance when far-reaching criticisms of 'their' field are made which completely misunderstand the current state of theorizing.

Nevertheless we must all put up with simplifications of evolutionary ideas, for they have been conspicuous ever since Charles Darwin himself presented a ground-breaking evolutionary idea as a popular science book. The subtleties of research and the particular debates they involve are routinely ignored by friend or foe of evolution alike. When evolution is discussed in school textbooks, or in museum displays, in instructional videos or popular science books, we will most likely be dealing with a gross simplification which glosses over difficulties and intricacies, and inevitably distorts some part of 'real' evolutionary thought.[2]

Practising scientists generally do not make extreme claims, are not necessarily naïve in their metaphysics, and often have a sophisticated view of the impact and constraints of their work. That has always been irrelevant, for it is not the practising scientists who dictate how people view science or what conclusions are drawn from it. In this, practising scientists may be just as much putty in the hands of political manipulators as the non-scientific public.

Yet surely there is something that is called 'the theory of evolution' which is debated and talked about endlessly. What is this? In the myriad practical disciplines within the general

---

2. No doubt this is the case for any area of science: introductory physics, for instance, will simplify complex ideas. Evolutionary theory, however, being such a politically sensitive area, suffers particularly from this problem, as every detail of a presentation is scrutinized for possible aberration.

field of evolution, can we really identify one, overarching theory that all scientists agree upon?

Ask this question of practising evolutionary scientists, and the answer will almost certainly be 'yes'. There is one general, basic theory that ties all these disparate fields together and which basically explains life on earth. That theory is Darwinism.

Ask what this theory is, however, and the consensus suddenly disappears. There will be almost as many descriptions of Darwinism as there are evolutionary scientists, and just about any account will raise protest from somewhere 'but you've misunderstood the theory'. This is partly because any such account *will* be an oversimplification, and people disagree on which bits can be left out or emphasized. The disagreement also partly exists because evolutionary theorists themselves disagree about what 'true' Darwinism is—with just as much passion and hostility as the most fiery creationist debate. Confusion also arises from the common habit of lumping together several generations of evolutionary theory—for the overarching theory itself has evolved over the years.

Let us, then, take a stab at summarising Darwinism, understanding that we are likely to get something wrong in someone's eyes. In order to avoid that as much as possible, I have included extensive quotations from prominent scientists' own writings—not to avoid work, but to avoid the charge of having misrepresented them! With those caveats in mind, let us proceed: What is Darwinian theory?

—1—
THE BASIC ANSWER

If you were to study an introductory course in evolutionary biology, you would probably be presented with a summary of the basics of the theory. This is the kind of standard explanation given to students, at the start of popular science books on the topic, or in general lectures. It is what is assumed in museum displays and TV documentaries. This is the basic, publicly presented understanding of evolutionary theory.

I have taken the following basic explanation from a book by Michael Rose, Professor of Evolutionary Biology at the University of California. There is no particular reason to take his description over any other; I happen to have his book to hand, and his description is typical of popular presentations.

What is Darwinian evolutionary theory?

First, it suggests that all of life, or at most each of a few divisions of it, must share a common physiological basis. This has been dramatically revealed since the 1950s by the universality of nucleic acids as the basis of life, DNA in particular…

Second, in addition to the unity of life, the particular patterns of similarity among species can be explained in terms of common ancestry. Thus, the common features among birds, such as feathers, are to be explained in terms of the possession of feathers among the common ancestral species of all living birds… Most common characters can be explained in terms of derivation from common ancestors that had similar structures, a phenomenon known as homology. It is in this sense that bat wings, the front hooves of horses, and the human hand are homologous: all are thought to be evolutionary modifications of the digits of the two front limbs of a mammalian ancestor common to all three groups. The differences between these three structures are explained by evolutionary biologists as resulting from adaptation, at least in part...

Third, evolution is necessarily continuous, much as familial lineage is... Evolution can only gradually work on the materials. It cannot boldly create completely new models of life.[3]

What is the evidence for evolutionary theory?

Although Darwin's schema of the relationship of all organisms is difficult to test, there are, Rose writes, "empirical points which it satisfactorily explains that any other system of life would find almost impossible to explain rationally". This is the standard evidence for evolutionary theory. The relevant points are:

First, it is possible to trace the broad outlines of evolution in all forms which readily fossilize. Forms which do not fossilize, like earthworms, are difficult to study using geological formations. But lineages like those of the vertebrates, which fossilize well because of their hard skeletons, have been worked out in considerable detail. The resulting patterns are clearly like those of Darwin's tree.

Second, the farther back we go in the fossil record, which means the deeper the strata of rock, the greater the difference between fossil forms and living species, on the average. This is as we expect if evolution is a continuous historical process, accumulating small changes in an essentially irreversible way.

Third, fossils from adjacent layers of rock are more likely to resemble each other than fossils from widely separated strata. In a sense, this is just a natural corollary of the second point.

3. Michael R. Rose, *Darwin's Spectre: Evolutionary Biology in the Modern World*, Princeton University Press, Princeton, 1998, pp. 78-79.

Fourth, the living forms present on one isolated land mass, like Australia, are usually closely related to the recent fossils of that region, rather than those of distant regions. This is another illustration of the continuity of Darwin's evolutionary process... Generally, such 'biogeography' is only explicable in terms of common descent—the overwhelming concentration of marsupial mammals in Australia alone makes a devastating case for this point of view...

Fifth, embryology reveals that early development involves structures which can be readily associated with common ancestors, even when these structures are not retained in the fully developed form. A dramatic illustration of this is the fact that mammalian and bird embryos develop gill arches early in embryonic development, which is only reasonable if we suppose that these groups originally had fish species for common ancestors. More generally, the embryos of quite large taxonomic groups tend to go through very similar stages early on in development. This is not to argue that development recapitulates evolution in any precise way. But the developmental process for many living things often betrays evolutionary origins quite dissimilar to those made manifest by the adult form. In other words, there appear to be 'residues' in our lives, archaic bits of physiology and anatomy, that make little sense unless our ancestors were very different kinds of organisms. This is a situation that evolutionary theory can explain easily, but which nonevolutionary theories have to struggle over. Naturally, the characteristic response of most creation theorists is to ignore this point, or twist it into a criticism of evolution on the grounds that the recapitulation is not perfect. But evolutionary theory in its modern form does not require any such perfect recapitulation. For evolution, the archaic features of life merely reveal its tortuous history, like the archaic features of human language or common law.

The evidence in support of Darwin's Tree is so good, and its explanatory power so vast, that the theory of evolution by modification from common ancestors was widely accepted by biologists in Darwin's lifetime. When you hear of controversies about evolutionary biology, you can be fairly confident that they will concern the role of natural selection or variation in the rate of evolution. Darwin's Tree of Life is one of the great slabs on which modern biology is built. It isn't going to be corroded by the weak bile of Darwinism's many critics.[4]

In a nutshell, then, Darwinism is a theory that postulates that all life forms are descended from a common ancestor; and that the progression in the fossil record is explained as a record of that descent. Also, similarities between organisms are to be explained by this 'family' relationship. The mechanism by which this happened is natural selection, a process that 'selects' or allows to survive those organisms best suited to the environment—a process that leads to adaptation.

That is the gist of evolutionary theory, in the general form that most high-school students or popular science readers would recognise. However this popular summary is far from all there is to know about evolution. It is easy to assume, from presentations such as this, that Darwin came up with a theory in its entirety which is followed by all evolutionary scientists today. Such an assumption is far from the truth. Not only have Darwin's ideas been radically changed since his time, but there is considerable disagreement even today about what evolutionary theory ought to be.

It is time, then, to complicate the picture. Let us start with Darwin himself. What was Charles Darwin's Darwinism?

4. *Ibid.*, pp. 80-81.

⊷ 2 ⊷
WHAT DID DARWIN SAY?

If during the long course of ages and under varying conditions of life, organic beings vary at all in the several parts of their organisation, and I think this cannot be disputed; if there be, owing to the high geometrical powers of increase of each species, at some age, season, or year, a severe struggle for life, and this certainly cannot be disputed; then, considering the infinite complexity of the relations of all organic beings to each other and to their conditions of existence, causing an infinite diversity in structure, constitution, and habits, to be advantageous to them, I think it would be a most extraordinary fact if no variation ever had occurred useful to each being's own welfare, in the same way as so many variations have occurred useful to man. But if variations useful to any organic being do occur, assuredly individuals thus characterised will have the best chance of being preserved in the struggle for life; and from the strong principle of inheritance they will tend to produce offspring similarly characterised. This principle of preservation, I have called, for the sake of brevity, Natural Selection.[5]

You may have found this nineteenth-century prose a little hard to read. These days we are not used to science—or indeed, anything much—being explained in such long sentences. The style, however, is significant to understanding

---

5. Charles Darwin, *The Origin of Species by Means of Natural Selection, Or, The Preservation of Favoured Races in the Struggle for Life*, Penguin Books, Harmondsworth, 1968 (first published John Murray 1859), pp. 169-170.

Darwin's contribution to science. Darwin's book on evolution, *The Origin of Species*, was a discussion of his ideas intended to persuade the reader to the likelihood of his theory. It was not a scientific paper, filled with experimental results and research outlines. He explained his ideas bit by bit, using many analogies to the known practice of selective breeding done by humans (on dogs, cattle and so on). Once the basic idea was explained, Darwin discussed various sorts of supporting evidence, such as the distribution of present-day species. This evidence was anecdotal, not based on quantitative studies. It was presented so as to persuade the reader to the possibility of Darwin's ideas being true, not to prove them so. Darwin also discussed potential objections to the theory and how he might answer them.

Darwin's language was tentative and gentle, in fine Victorian style. This was not a bold assertion of obvious truth: it was a slow building up of possibilities to a probable conclusion. It was a polite work by a gentleman of learning, addressed to other gentlemen of learning, putting forward new ideas in the hope of a courteous hearing.

While Darwin had hit upon an original and fruitful idea, there was still much work to be done to demonstrate, if possible, the reality of the matter. It may have been plausible that, if all the contingencies Darwin proposed were true, then natural selection could happen. It was an entirely different matter to demonstrate that not only were the contingencies true, but that natural selection had, in fact, shaped the history of life forms on earth.

The first supposition, explained at length in Darwin's elegant prose, was hard to deny; that somewhere, sometime, some animal would have a slight edge over its fellows in some aspect. Put in such general terms, there's not much to object to. It can be observed that some deer can run faster than others. The one that can run faster is more likely to outrun predators, and that is generally advantageous to a deer.

The main difficulty was in convincing people of the next step in the logic—that the offspring would inherit this advantage. On the surface, it seems straightforward; of course offspring inherit characteristics from their parents. But is there any guarantee they will inherit the right one? Or that further generations will continue to have this trait? After all, sometimes a strong parent can have a sickly child. Just how does heredity work?

Darwin was at a loss here, because this was years before the whole idea of genes. The prevailing theory in Darwin's time was that of blending inheritance; that offspring will be a blend of mother's and father's characteristics. This theory, of course, was a great problem for Darwin's natural selection. For if one deer is born that can outrun all others, its offspring will run slightly less fast, being a blend of fast and normal parents; the next generation will be even slower, being a blend of less-fast and normal; eventually the status quo will prevail. The advantageous characteristic will not be passed on through the generations.

Another problem raised at the time was where the variation came from. How did the new, advantageous characteristic originate? It was well known that bizarre, new offspring could be born by chance—a two-headed sheep, or some other monstrous being—but such animals rarely survived or reproduced. What was the source of new, potentially helpful material amongst a population? Having no theory of genes, of course, the scientific community had no theory of mutation of genes, so that idea was not available. Again, Darwin went with the theory that was available at the time—Lamarckian evolution.

Although Darwin's theory is generally explained as refuting Lamarck's, indeed it actually incorporated it.

Jean Baptiste Lamarck, a noted French scholar, had presented in 1800 what was until Darwin's time the most plausible of evolutionary theories. These days, Lamarck is hardly mentioned in biology classes except to be ridiculed, but in his time his theory was groundbreaking and quite plausible. In essence, he postulated evolution of different forms through descent, with change being stimulated by environment. His mechanism involved a kind of 'power of life' which drove organisms to increasing complexity, as they would strive to fit their surroundings. As the environment changed, then, organisms would learn to change and so survive with it.

Lamarck's views are now ridiculed not just because he postulated the capacity for organisms to change in the fight for survival, but that he assumed that such changes would be passed on to offspring. We now know that skills or capacities acquired in one's lifetime do not get passed on—the bodybuilder's muscles do not make his children more muscly. However we can see that such a confusion is easily possible. After all, the bodybuilder's children may well turn out to be successful bodybuilders themselves. Without a clear understanding of how genetics works, Lamarck's theory was not so bad. Darwin certainly considered aspects of it plausible.

This complicates our picture of Darwin's theory a little, but it needs to be understood. Darwin's argument was mainly about long-term change on the level of species. He saw this as the cumulative effect of small changes: the individuals who do not suit an environment do not survive, and only the ones that by chance do suit it stay alive. The group as a whole, then, changes. This is a different emphasis from Lamarck's theory, which concentrates on individual organisms changing their habits to fit an environment, and passing on subsequent structural changes. However, in the details the two theories use similar ideas. While Darwin was mostly concerned with how to explain large-scale changes in species, he did need to postulate some source for the minute variations on which his theory depended. This is where he used Lamarckian ideas. Organisms gain new characteristics, he said, through the effect that the environment may have on their parents, or through use or disuse of an organ.[6]

There were various other objections at the time—the problem of the fossil record, for example, which did not tend to show a gradual evolving of different species as Darwin suggested. There was also the objection of the sheer complexity of the problem; natural selection might sound fine in general, but could it really account for the immense complexity and diversity of the living world? Darwin could only give vague answers. The fossil record, he argued, was necessarily incomplete as fossilisation was a chance process; and as for the power of natural selection, he could only stress that given enough time, it possibly could account for the diversity of the world. However, "[i]f it could be demonstrated that any complex organ existed, which could not possibly have been formed by numerous, successive, slight modifications, my theory would absolutely break down".[7]

Despite these problems, Darwin's theory was to become a major influence over the following few decades. This phenomenon bears examining, for the popularity did not come

6. *Ibid.*, pp. 173 ff.
7. *Ibid.*, p. 219.

about by the scientific community being convinced of Darwin's accuracy; in fact, the theories which held sway as the nineteenth century approached its end, even though often going under the name 'Darwinism', bore little resemblance to it at all. Darwin's theory itself, with its concepts of natural selection as described in *Origin of Species* and later works, was simply not scientifically convincing, particularly without a reinforcing theory of inheritance. The publicity that his theory evoked, however, effectively broke through the taboo on evolutionistic theories that had operated up until then. Theories which had been ridiculed or ignored earlier in the century could now thrive. Across Europe there was an increasing interest in evolutionary theory, which came generally to be called Darwinian, even though non-Darwinian ideas about evolution were much more dominant towards the end of the nineteenth century.[8]

The way in which Darwinism came to be so popular, and so start the trend of evolutionary theorising, had little to do with scientific research. The publicity was generated largely by a deliberate propaganda campaign, spearheaded by the anti-Church activist Thomas Huxley. Although he did not agree with Darwin's theory himself, he found it highly useful as a tool in his political efforts to reduce church power over intellectual institutions and to promote professional science as the arbiter of knowledge. Huxley was a persuasive orator, a very hard worker and a clever propagandist. It is worth remembering that the form in which we inherited Darwinism was filtered

---

8. Ideas such as recapitulation and preformationism.

through political and anti-religious campaigns.[9]

In any case, the popularity won by evolutionary theories in general suffered an almost-mortal blow as the nineteenth century ended. In 1890, August Weismann presented experimental evidence that acquired traits cannot be inherited. Remember that Darwin's theory, like all other evolutionary theories of the time, depended on the idea that variation came from individual organisms adapting to their environment and passing their acquired characteristics onto offspring. This was the Lamarckian theory of inheritance, which we discussed above. Darwin's theory had revolutionised evolutionary thought by suggesting that large-scale change came from the accumulation of small-scale changes. But what made these small-scale changes happen? If variation within a population did not come from individuals learning new tricks—learning to run faster, or go without water for longer, or whatever small variation was needed—and passing these on, then where did it come from?

This undermined just about all evolutionistic thinking at the time, as it removed the crucial source of variation on which the theories depended. It would not be until the modern theory of genetics was settled upon that evolutionary theory could be resurrected. At this stage, around the turn of the twentieth century, Darwinism would appear to be on the decline. A bold new step had been taken in the field of biology, but it was not clear if this path could be followed any further.

9.   For discussion of this see K. Birkett, *Unnatural Enemies: An Introduction to Science and Christianity*, Matthias Media, Sydney, 1997; and D. Starling, 'Thomas Huxley and the 'warfare' between science and religion: mythology, politics and ideology', *kategoria*, 1196, *3*, pp. 33-50.

—3—

THE GENETIC REVOLUTION

The story so far might be called the rise and fall of Darwinism. It is a story not many people know—from most public descriptions, such as the one with which we began, one would think Darwinism had had a steady forward march ever since 1859. As we have seen, however, Darwin's idea was controversial, interesting and sparked off all sorts of new thinking about biology, but it gradually ran out of steam. Darwin had a very good idea in natural selection, but that could only take biology so far. Darwinism ran its course, and ideas moved on. Some biologists kept developing evolutionary ideas within a more fixed framework—that is, evolution not by the chance effects of random change in the environment, but driven to some extent internally, according to certain limited patterns. These ideas, more popular in Europe than they ever were in England or America, are still a subset of evolutionary research today.

In England, evolutionary theories had faltered on the problem of inheritance. Yet a development had already occurred which was to take mainstream evolutionary theory in a new direction. Earlier in the nineteenth century, an obscure monk named Gregor Mendel came up with a theory that heredity worked through discrete packets of specific traits in organisms. This was the origin of our modern idea of genes—individual units that alone, or in combination with others, govern certain characteristics. Mendel published in a little-read journal, and died uncelebrated for his feat. His work was rediscovered in 1900, and his ideas developed by the English scientist William Bateson.

Bateson, who later dubbed himself the 'father of genetics', was an ardent evolutionist but already had doubts about Darwin's idea of natural selection. He looked for isolated populations from which he could gain experimental results, and chose organisms in isolated lakes. Setting about measuring the variations in these populations, he had found little to convince him of natural selection's role in producing change within a population of the same species. If natural selection was going to work at all, he came to believe, it must be on the basis of what might be called 'discontinuous variations'. In other words, Bateson was looking for something to explain the great differences between different organisms. Even within one population you can have very different organisms—big ones, small ones, differently coloured ones. This kind of variation is not minute, on a small, gradual scale—it can be quite large. That is, the variation is discontinuous.

Bateson was not convinced that natural selection was enough to explain these differences. This was even more true for the issue of speciation—that is, how a whole new species develops from a previous one. If it's hard enough to explain how to get big fish and small fish within a species, how on earth do you explain the jump from fish to frogs? Stricter Darwinians had by this time put the problem of speciation aside, assuming that it would look after itself in the long term if natural selection could be shown to be at work in the short term. Just give it enough time, they said, and enough small changes would accumulate to create a whole new species, given the right conditions. Bateson, however, worried about this idea of new species. He played with the idea of saltationism—the idea that evolution proceeds by sudden leaps, perhaps even to whole new species. Less radically, he was inclined to the idea that within a population you don't get a smooth spread of variation; you just get odd, chance differences. Maybe there was more going on than gradual, small scale change.

Bateson looked around for a theory of inheritance through discrete units, or 'genes', [10] as a way to defend the emphasis he was now placing on discontinuous variation. If inheritance comes in discrete units—if separate characteristics are inherited through separate building blocks—then significant changes would be less likely to disappear in the blending process. If units were big enough, you might even get a whole new species when two previously uncombined genes came together in one offspring. If enough inherited material existed in one gene, then cross-breeding could potentially create a major change in the organism. Bateson also hypothesised that a chance change in one discrete gene could mean a large change in the organism, another source of immediate change.

There was heated debate about the theory of genetics, and its place in evolutionary theory, for some thirty years. Most people saw Mendelian genetics as contradicting Darwin's idea of continuous variation. It was to take developments in statistics, genetic theory and (surprisingly) physics before there was a reconciliation of Darwinian natural selection and the laws of inheritance through genes.

New developments

New work in statistics meant that you could now talk about the expected curve of variation in a population. You would expect that within one population (for instance), most giraffes would be around the average height, with a roughly equal, smaller number of very tall and very short ones. If the expected variation was skewed—if in fact, most were very tall—then you could check if

---

10. Hugo de Vries, who rediscovered Mendel's work, spoke of 'pangenes'; W. L. Johannsen suggested abbreviating this to 'gene' in 1909. It was a theoretical entity—so far no physical structure that would actually perform this role had been discovered.

natural selection was causing the shift, which is what Darwinism would predict. Growth in statistics also meant that there was now a more solid basis for understanding that significant change within a population could happen without a single large variation but a whole lot of little ones. These statistical developments, along with the growing field of genetics, moved the focus of biology from whole organisms to the idea of a genetic population.

This was combined with another, quite different idea, which came from new developments in physics. This was the concept of equilibrium. In physics, the new area of thermodynamics said that equilibrium is a state of a system where nothing happens—everything is in balance, so there's no tendency to move one way or another. If you're not in equilibrium, you'll have a tendency to move—and that direction will always be towards equilibrium. Equilibrium, then, is whatever state which that system will always tend to approach.

For instance, say you release gas into a container so that in the first instant all the gas is concentrated up in one corner. We know that the gas will not stay there, all bunched up in one corner—it will spread out to fill the container. When it has filled the space with more or less equal density, the gas stays in that state. It has reached equilibrium, and there is no tendency to move away from it. If you drop a droplet of ink into a tank of water, initially the ink will be visible as a blob around where the droplet hit. Eventually, however, it will be equally distributed over the whole amount of water. It will tend towards its equilibrium state, where everything is 'equal' and there is no further inclination to change. The ink molecules won't spontaneously come together into the initial droplet again.[11]

---

11. This is the law of entropy, or the second law of thermodynamics. Technically, it says that a closed system will tend to a state where no further energy can be extracted.

The 'force' is all the other way around.

What has this to do with Darwinism? The specifics of gas molecules or ink droplets have nothing to do with it, but the general concept of equilibrium became very important. Imagine you have a group of genes. There's a certain distribution; say, 10% is gene A, 20% is gene B and so on. Will that distribution change? It will, if this is an unstable state. Maybe, just as with gas molecules, there is a state in which all is in balance, and the distribution of genes will keep adjusting until it reaches that state. Maybe there is an equilibrium for gene populations. If so, then you could postulate a law of population genetics: that a population will always tend towards the equilibrium state.

That's all very well, but what does it mean in practice? Think of an equilibrium state as the state where a species is perfectly adapted to the environment. There is no competition, because everybody has enough and all is right with the world. The idea of evolution, then, could be reframed as the tendency of a species to reach that equilibrium point. But in fact, with the discovery of genes, evolution was not thought of primarily in terms of species or organisms any more, but 'gene populations'. So the equilibrium state might be that in which just the right genes were present in a species for it to reproduce and survive optimally.

Now, take it to one more level of abstraction, and think of the equilibrium state as purely a description of the genes. This population of genes could be in a test-tube or in a computer model; the point is, there's a whole range of them. Mathematically, the distribution of genes can be described as changing until it reaches an equilibrium.

The geneticist R. A. Fisher did this. He applied the idea of equilibrium to the distribution of genes in a freely interbreeding population. Just as physical processes 'strive' towards entropy (like the gas 'striving' to fill a space), Fisher argued, genes strive towards fitness. Fitness was defined as reproductive success. In a population of genes, the natural tendency is to move to a state of 'fitness' according to Fisher's definition.[12] He also developed a 'law' of genetic change: that the rate of increase in fitness in a population is directly proportional to the amount of variance between genotypes. The more different genes there are, the more variety there is, the faster the population will move towards fitness.

We need to understand what these developments meant for Darwin's theory. Instead of thinking of a population of organisms, we now need to think of a population of genes—the 'genetic pool' of a species, for instance. In our new theory, we postulate that the gene pool tends towards fitness (which means in practice that the maximum number of offspring are born in the next generation). The term 'fitness' now applies to the whole population of genes, not to individual animals, and not to individual genes. We are now dealing with mathematics which describes how a whole system changes over time. We can now have specific predictions about gene populations and what they will do over time.

This is where the ideas from statistics come in. The change of a population is understood statistically. The individual units are unpredictable, but the overall behaviour of the population can be predicted. The prediction is that the population will tend towards the equilibrium point called 'fitness', after which the population has no pressure to change.

In the real world, 'fitness' might happen in the circumstances we described above—when a species is perfectly inte-

---

12. See Fisher's most popular work, *The Genetical Theory of Natural Selection*, Oxford University Press, Oxford, 1930.

grated with its environment. It may happen, however (and probably will) that the environment changes. It gets colder or hotter, or there are more predators around, or too much rain, or just too many offspring. The species is no longer in the equilibrium state of fitness. There is a new state of fitness to be reached. In our new abstract terminology, the system is no longer at equilibrium, because the equilibrium point has moved. So the system changes in a direction towards the new equilibrium point—the new fitness. In practice, this shifting of the fitness goal could happen continually.

This was not the theory as Darwin conceived it, but a recasting of the theory under a new model. Now the population of genes was thought of as being like a thermodynamic system, always seeking equilibrium, which changes as the constraints change. This new evolutionary theory was universal and gave a mathematical basis to the spreading of genes; it was not about particular adaptive stories any more. Evolutionary theory was now becoming a generalised, rigorous study of genetic populations.

⊷4⊷

THE MODERN SYNTHESIS

Today, what is taught as evolutionary theory is generally referred to as 'The Neo-Darwinian Synthesis'. This recognises that modern evolutionary theory is really not Darwin's theory. The Darwinian name provides historical recognition of an important thinker in the field, but the theory has moved on since then. Evolutionary theory is now a synthesis of some of Darwin's ideas, some genetic ideas, and some new biological ideas, all blended into a new, twentieth-century framework.

Darwin's Darwinism had proved incapable of converting the hypothesis of natural selection into a fully adequate theory of evolution. The theory of blending inheritance had crippled it. What was needed was a new conceptual framework in which the core of the Darwinian tradition, the theory of natural selection, could be defended and used to solve evolution's main problems. Fisher's change to a statistical model of genetic populations allowed this to happen.

In Fisher's theory there was still room for forces other than natural selection to act on a population. For instance, he suggested that, in smaller sub-populations, genes can become established by chance rather than by natural selection, in a process called genetic drift. However this was considered unimportant by Fisher. Sewall Wright, an American geneticist, took this chance element more seriously because he was convinced that many organisms do live in relatively small breeding groups. He was a biologist, with a background of experience in how real populations live, unlike Fisher whose background was in statistics.[13] J. B. S. Haldane, a Cambridge geneticist, also added theories on how single genes could spread through populations.

Other modifications to the theory followed. Russian-born Theodosius Dobzhansky emigrated to America and studied fruit-fly genetics. He focussed on the fact that populations can have large amounts of variation that may be carried for generations without reaching equilibrium. He and his students demonstrated that the width of genetic variance in natural populations was far greater than was expected.[14] The field of evolutionary theory was expanding in many different ways in this first part of the twentieth century. What was being worked out theoretically and mathematically by statisticians such as Fisher, was being tested and expanded experimentally in the laboratory and in the field by scientists such as Dobzhansky and others. The experimental results did not always match what was expected mathematically. New ideas were being suggested and tried out. A new academic discipline of evolutionary biology was developing, with all the false starts, breakthroughs and excitement of a new discipline.

With all this work on different aspects of population genetics taking place, the modern theory known as the 'neo-Darwinian synthesis' was created—mainly led by Dobzhansky, Ernst Mayr and George Gaylord Simpson. The synthesis included a combination of deterministic and chance aspects of how genes are fixed in populations; that is, that the

---

13. See Sewall Wright, 'Review of *The Genetical Theory of Natural Selection* by R. A. Fisher', *Journal of Heredity*, 1930, *21*, pp. 349-356.
14. See T. Dobzhansky, *Genetics and the Origin of Species*, Columbia University Press, Columbia, 1937; also Theodosius Dobzhansky, Francisco J. Ayala, G. Ledyard Stebbins, and James W. Valentine, *Evolution*, W. H. Freeman and Company, San Francisco, 1977.

evolution of a population of genes is in part law-like, but also depends on unpredictable chance events. It postulated a basic, constant statistical process going on, according to mathematical laws, as a population of genes moves to equilibrium. This process would presumably continue fairly steadily. On the way, a subpopulation could develop new and interesting variations. Mutation could also introduce new genetic elements. Chance was seen as playing its part within a lawlike, statistical framework.[15] Mathematical models were combined with experimental results, and much fruitful research was taking place.

The field of evolutionary biology had taken elements from Darwin (natural selection), Mendel (genes), statistics, the new physics and mathematics and blended them into a new discipline. Now practitioners were not just biologists; they were evolutionary biologists, with a research programme to take them forward. Evolutionary biology began to have professors, journals, university departments and funding. It was a field that suggested possible new experiments in a whole range of areas, as different aspects of the theory could be tested and modified. This was an exciting time for evolutionary biologists—a whole vista of new theoretical areas to be explored, and jobs and laboratories being made available to do it in. The Darwinian synthesis had created a new science.

15. See Ernst Mayr and William B. Provine (eds), *The Evolutionary Synthesis: Perspectives on the Unification of Biology*, Harvard University Press, Cambridge, Mass., 1980. Another interesting book is Ernst Mayr, *Systematics and the Origin of Species from the Viewpoint of a Zoologist*, Harvard University Press, Cambridge, Mass.,1942, 1999.

⚬5⚬

THE THEORY TODAY

The neo-Darwinian synthesis produced theories about how gene populations behaved over time, with various practical applications in specific populations of organisms. It did not, however, examine precisely how genes worked and there was no clear understanding of the way in which genes affected the characteristics of a grown organism. The gene remained somewhat mysterious, understood in its mass movements but not in individual detail. There was certainly plenty to study in gene populations—it was not as if evolutionary biology was running out of theories to explore. However it did not as yet get deep into the mechanics of how genes do what they do. Yet just as Darwin's idea of natural selection was transformed into something new with the discovery of genes, so the new synthesis was again transformed by the addition of the new field of *molecular biology*—the inner workings of genes.

The breakthrough was in 1953, when Francis Crick and James Watson discovered the structure of DNA.[16] At first, this was simply taken as confirmation of what genetic Darwinians had been assuming about how genes behave and how they affect organisms. Now the actual physical basis for transmitting genetic information could be understood, and how variation arises from mutation and recombination. However this simple confirmation was not to continue. Once the inner workings of genes began to be studied more carefully, it was

16. J. D. Watson and F. H. C. Crick, 'A structure for deoxyribose nucleic acid', *Nature*, 1953, *171*, pp. 737-738.

realised that the relationship between genes and the grown organisms they govern is a very complicated one. There is still a vast amount of knowledge about genes and their effects yet to be uncovered.

There have been surprising developments in understanding. Molecules such as proteins and nucleic acids, for instance, were found to evolve too, but not in a Darwinian way. Molecular biologist Motoo Kimura developed what he called 'neutral theory'; that such molecules change according to a random process, regardless of the fitness state of the population.[17]

Work on the genetic mechanisms that guide the development and growth of an organism also brought interesting insights. There is much more complexity in genetic systems than had been expected. It seems that a good deal of the order of a genome is the result of self-ordering properties of large genetic arrays. That is, the way in which genes are organised within an organism seem to be responding to something other than outside changes in the environment. Characteristics such as the number of offspring, timing of development, reproductive activity, onset and function of aging and death, seem guided from 'within', independent of environmental forces driving natural selection.

Controversy still continues over whether, or to what extent, natural selection shapes the genetic content of a species. Arguments also rage over whether new species can develop through the slow collection of changes—as of yet, there is no specific theory for how this happens. Fisher's statistical model is not fully supported by experimental data. The data instead seem to show that genes are not forever tending to a shifting

17. See Mootoo Kimura, *The Neutral Theory of Molecular Evolution*, Cambridge University Press, Cambridge, 1983.

equilibrium point; they are not so mobile. It may be that natural selection is restricted to microevolution—changes within a species—and a different general theory is needed for both speciation (on the grand scale) and molecular levels (on the tiny scale). In fact, the whole concept of what constitutes a 'species' has become very controversial.

Given the rapid advances in molecular genetics, genomics and the immense increase in knowledge of cell biology and how cells are internally regulated, it is likely that huge questions will continue to arise about evolution. The problem of how species, or organisms, evolved may pale beside the question of how a single complex cell evolved. Cells today appear to need and use all their internal machinery to survive. If this is the end product of evolution, how did a primitive cell survive?

Most of such controversy takes place bit by bit in specialist journals, as more experimental results are published and theories developed and discussed. Some of the figures within evolutionary biology, however, have taken their debate to the wider world and caused considerable confusion as to the status of evolutionary theory. These highly visible writers and speakers have carried on their discussions in popular books and columns as well as technical publications, and take us into another aspect of evolutionary controversy: the highly emotive reactions to 'selfish genes'.

So far, we have discussed the theory of evolution in a fairly technical manner. We have tried to understand how the specifics of the theory have changed since Darwin's day, and how it has incorporated various developments in other sciences. We have gone through this in order to understand the theory itself better, in a scientific sense.

However it is fairly dry stuff. If this is all there is to evolutionary theory—statistics, genetics and fruit flies—one wonders what all the fuss is about. At this dry scientific level, there seems little to be passionate about unless this is your chosen career.

As we turn to some of the more public debates, we begin to see why evolutionary theory is so controversial. Not many people tear their hair over the mathematics of genetic arrays. When theorists start to make statements about morality, kinship and love, however, people take more notice. The real controversy and heat of evolutionary debate comes when we start to see terms that we recognise as potentially applying to ourselves.

⊶ *Part II* ⊷

DISSENSION
IN THE RANKS

To understand some of the more spectacular arguments in the field of evolutionary biology today, we need to go back into more recent scientific and social history. The neo-Darwinian synthesis with the exciting addition of molecular biology was remarkably successful in scientific terms—that is, it kept on producing new theories and new avenues for research. It appeared to be an expanding field, which means a field with a lot of potential for discovery. Within this expansion and generation of new ideas, however, there are bound to be disputes. Moreover, there are some fairly fundamental issues which have never been settled, and over which the controversy only seems to get bigger. We are now going to look at one group of issues, not about details of experiments or particular genetic problems, but about larger ideas of what Darwinism actually is and how it works. These issues are relatively easy to follow, not least because many of the disputants pride themselves on their ability to explain the issues clearly and in the public eye.

In one sense, it does not matter if you do not follow the details of these disputes. (If you get bogged down, I suggest you skip forward to chapter 9.) What is interesting to evolutionary biologists is not necessarily interesting for everyone. However I have included this section in order to demonstrate that the current state of evolutionary theory includes considerable disagreement about fairly central issues. For many readers, particularly those familiar with these debates, such a statement will be seen as stating the obvious. Such readers may consider this section a useless stirring of the coals, going over controversies that everyone knows about.

The problem is, however, that *not* everyone knows about them. A very large proportion of the educated public is under the impression that evolution is a fact, a proven theory, to be taken for granted. However, the truth is that evolutionary biology is not 'a fact', but a wide-ranging collection of competing theories, some well supported by evidence, others on the edge of speculation, and many under violent dispute.

I have once more included large slabs of quotation from the scientists involved, so as to be sure I do not distort their positions. These debates are real, and fiery, and over issues of substance. But to put them into their real-world context, let us return to what was happening in evolutionary theory in the second half of the twentieth century.

⟻ 6 ⟼

The political background

A lot of the current controversy developed from what was a big problem for Darwinism in the 1940s to 1960s—altruism.[1] The general idea of evolution by natural selection, as we have seen, is that in the face of scarce resources not all members of a group can survive. Only those who can best keep themselves alive will win out, and those survival characteristics will then be passed on. But if evolution proceeds on the basis of competition between individuals, then why is it that many individuals within species do not, in fact, compete? A group of organisms—a breeding colony, a pack, a social group—often shows considerable cooperation between the members. Some members might even sacrifice themselves, or never reproduce, in favour of other individuals and their reproduction. Ant nests, after all, contain sterile worker ants which help the queen reproduce—how is Darwinian selection happening there? Why do these helpful traits get passed on if the helpful ones never reproduce?

The most popular answer was group selection: that individuals contribute to the good of the species as a whole, and the successful species survives. This, however, loses the fundamental advantages of Darwinism—that slight differences between individuals can be magnified and passed on through survival of the fittest. There was no adequate alternative mechanism to account for group selection. This theory was successfully challenged in the 60s by a new idea, 'kin selection', which gives a genetic explanation for altruism and therefore an actual

---

1. Altruism is unselfish behaviour which helps another without gain to oneself.

mechanism for it.

Essentially, kin selection depends on the ideas of a gene pool shared by the species. Although a sterile worker ant never has off-spring, the genes which make it helpful are likely to be present in its brothers or sisters (such as the queen ant). So even though the sterile ant does not pass on the 'helpful' gene itself, the sister ant will. The sterile ant's helpful behaviour, looking after the queen and her offspring, makes this more likely to happen.

Kin selection was taken up by sociobiology, a field which studied the possible evolutionary explanations for social behaviour (such as cooperation and altruism). Sociobiology, a relatively new field, was brought together by E. O. Wilson in 1975 with his book *Sociobiology*.[2] It was a very controversial book, not for its ideas about animal behaviour, but because Wilson applied evolutionary concepts to human behaviour. That was politically taboo at that time. It reminded people of the horrors of eugenics, and Hitler's claims of racial superior-ity. A massive controversy erupted, as much about political affiliation as about science.[3]

Caught up in this debate was English biologist Richard Dawkins, who published *The Selfish Gene*[4] soon after *Sociobiology* and was politically partnered with it. The politi-cal fights are not the issue here, but the arguments raise issues in the current state of evolutionary biology.[5] For it became

---

2. E. O. Wilson, *Sociobiology: The New Synthesis*, Harvard University Press, Cambridge, Mass., 1975.

3. See Kirsten Birkett, 'And now for the real answer…sociobiology and the search for explanation', *kategoria*, 2001, *21*, pp.33-49, for a discussion of sociobiology.

4. Richard Dawkins, *The Selfish Gene*, Oxford University Press, Oxford, 1976.

5. For a complete account of the fights over sociobiology and its implications, see Ullica Segerstrale, *Defenders of the Truth: The Battle for Science in the Sociobiology Debate and Beyond*, Oxford University Press, Oxford, 2000.

important to understand just how much our behaviour is affected by our genes. If altruism can be explained by genetic evolution, does that mean our actions are really moral? If I am kind to my sister because of my genetic programming, does that empty my kindness of value? Into this charged atmosphere, Richard Dawkins inserted his book *The Selfish Gene.* The answer, he seemed to argue, is in our genes. This is the essence of evolution, he argued; understand what our genes are doing, and we understand who we are.

⊷ 7 ⊷

IS OUR FATE IN OUR GENES?

Richard Dawkins's smooth prose made easily understandable the essence of the genetic formulation of evolutionary theory. Why do animals develop as they do? Because certain genes are selected for, and other genes do not survive. We can think of evolution, Dawkins said, as the struggle waged between successful and unsuccessful genes. The individual animals can almost be thought of as incidental. We are just the vehicles for genes to propagate themselves. Genes don't care about good or bad or kindness or altruism; genes just try to get themselves reproduced. What organisms are like as a result is simply a side-effect. It is the 'selfish' behaviour of the genes, the efforts of genes to survive and reproduce, that really drives life.

The 'selfish gene' of Dawkins's book was a metaphor. The metaphor works by applying ideas of survival, and desire of survival, to genetic material. To grasp this idea, assume that a gene (or a group of genes) wants to survive, with survival defined as 'be reproduced in the next generation'. Then you can describe the actual features it creates in the individual as a survival strategy. If it is a successful strategy—if the individual passes that gene group to its offspring—then the gene does survive. If it is an unsuccessful strategy, then it does not. In this way, those genes which have the most successful strategies—produce the characteristics and behaviour that are most likely to lead to an individual or anyone else having that gene group surviving and having children and that characteristic being passed on—are the ones which are selected for and are therefore present in a population. This is how we explain the presence of particular genes or gene groups in a population.

Many objections were raised to this type of Darwinian explanation. Some researchers reacted to the suggestion that the gene is the only entity that matters. However, there was considerable range of opinion. Zoologist Ernst Mayr (amongst others) insisted that what existed was only the genotype—the full genetic structure of an organism—not individual genes. Palaeontologist Stephen Jay Gould complained that in Darwinism the *individual* is the unit of selection, for the struggle for existence is between individuals—selection cannot see genes. Dawkins replied that he was just using 'gene' as shorthand for 'replicator', as he was trying to discover philosophically what characteristics a replicator needs. He was not talking about physical genes, although that is how many people (probably not surprisingly) read him.

Critics of Dawkins had a point. A gene does not try to survive—it does not have a selfish survival strategy. That is just a metaphorical way of talking. DNA does not even self-replicate, strictly speaking; it relies on protein enzymes to do so. The only entity capable of self-reproduction is the cell, the phenotype. The genotype cannot self-replicate. When you add sexual reproduction the situation is even more complicated. A body is not actually what a gene builds to replicate itself, for in a sexual body a gene has no guarantee it will be replicated. If the gene were that selfish, one would think it should have picked a much simpler organism.

Also, the 'survival strategy' of the gene can be seriously affected by all sorts of higher-level decisions we make—deciding not to have children, deciding not to help our relatives' children, feuding with relatives, helping the sick and so on. In any case, this metaphor of survival does not explain the presence of *all* genes in the population, for there are other processes which lead to certain genes being present, including just inexplicable randomness.

Individual organisms like animals, on the other hand, *do* try to survive. It is not a metaphor with them. They do want to reproduce. The effect of this real desire to survive and reproduce, given the limitations of resources, is that only those with the most suitable characteristics actually manage to survive and reproduce. Darwin's natural selection had neatly described long-term change by means of short-term survival instinct, something which does not translate directly to genes, even if it makes a vivid metaphor.

Dawkins has continued to insist that he believes in nested hierarchies of genes—he never meant one gene alone when he spoke of 'the selfish gene'.[6] Nonetheless, he did mean replicators—genetic material—not the organic vehicles that embodied them. This, he thought, was a proper evolutionary explanation. Whether the vehicle was an organism or a group was not the point; what mattered was the thing that got replicated.

For Stephen Jay Gould's colleague, Niles Eldredge, it *was* vehicles that mattered. Eldredge said that the problem with the modern synthesis was that it limited its attention to only a few of the biological entities that existed. Ecological entities and broader categories of organisms were not included, yet they interacted with each other and affected each others' survival. If the only viewpoint is of genetic material, he insisted, then we will not address the question of (for instance) why we have species.

No one denied that natural selection produced adaptation, Eldredge said; just that this gradual process produced macroevolution. Just because gradualism was *consistent* with all

---

6. See, for instance, Richard Dawkins, *The Extended Phenotype: The Long Reach of the Gene*, Oxford University Press, Oxford, 1982, 1999, especially chapter 3.

other known evolutionary phenomena did not mean it was *sufficient* to explain them. Could natural selection among genes, for instance, explain the interactions between species at an ecological level? Probably not—yet this interaction could be just as important to the development of a species.

> Science seeks to explain phenomena (classes of events, in particular) in terms of causal interactions among entities. Thus in evolutionary biology, physical attributes of organisms are held to undergo adaptive modification according to the differential reproductive success of organisms that vary with respect to that trait within a breeding population—the principle of natural selection. It is my central contention…that in restricting analysis to those entities and interactive processes that are easily accessible to human observers over a few minutes, days, months, or years (a procedure easily defended on epistemological grounds) automatically and arbitrarily limits the range of entities, hence of interactive processes, that are admitted to causal theories of stasis and change. And such excluded entities and processes may well prove to be important to a full theory of history in both biological and sociocultural systems.
>
> In particular…it is the main legacy of the evolutionary biological theory of punctuated equilibria, which came out of palaeontology, that large-scale, interactive biotic entities of which organisms are parts do in fact exist; that their natures can be specified; and that their causal interactions can thus be elucidated.[7]

Eldredge's alternative description of evolution was very complex, much more than natural selection over a long time.

---

7. Niles Eldredge, 'Punctuated equilibria, rates of change, and large-scale entities in evolutionary systems', in Albert Somit and Steven A. Peterson (eds), *The Dynamics of Evolution: The Punctuated Equilibrium Debate in the Natural and Social Sciences*, Cornell University Press, Ithaca and London, 1989, pp. 103-120, p. 104.

He proposed two hierarchies of ideas that interact; one concerned with the development of information contained in the genome (which produces genes, organisms, demes, species, taxa), and one concerned with the economic organisation and integration of living systems (proteins, organisms, populations, communities, regional systems—ecologies). You can't separate out the first one and call it evolution, particularly if you only take the genes seriously. Evolution is about real organisms, living in communities, alongside other organisms as part of a whole ecology. To explain how these systems develop needs more than genes. A real explanation will also take into account how organisms interact, how species interact, how whole ecologies function.

Eldredge's view makes a lot of sense. There is a lot more to the natural world than just genes; and if you truly want a theory that describes the development of the natural world, you must take into account the incredibly complex systems of life, from the gene up to the jungle. This, however, is just too complex a problem in practice. What biology as a research discipline needs is a clear statement about evolution in order to organise research. The modern synthesis has simplified the problem in the interest of generating new scientific research. Science often works this way.

What is evolutionary theory really about? As it is currently construed, the theory is really about the behaviour of genes. It describes how gene populations differ from generation to generation, and what different processes influence that difference. Of course we know that genes are the basis of the characteristics we see in real organisms, and so they underlie all the more complex biological interactions. But the complaint made by many biologists is that just talking about genes is not enough. We cannot understand life if all we study is the interactions of genes. What *actually* affects how organisms develop is far more than their genes. It is how these organisms relate to each other and their environment. It is about how pups in the same litter interact, what might happen to their parents, how the food supply is changing, how the species next door is developing, how the overall ecology is acting and reacting. Of course all geneticists know this, but a theory which described all these interacting processes would be far too clumsy and complicated to do anything with.

The result, as scientists like Eldredge point out, is that evolutionary theory does not actually study the real world as it is—it studies one specific, particular, reduced aspect of the real biological world. It may be that this is necessary in order for the study to be practically possible—but it puts the theory in a more realistic context when this is recognised. There is a lot more to evolution than genes, and there is a lot more to understanding the actual development of life than the current emphasis on genetic theory.

⊷ 8 ⊷

THE PROBLEM OF ADAPTATIONISM

Another, related, problem which keeps rearing its head in modern evolutionary discourse is that of the place of adaptationism. The traditional Darwinian view is that if you wish to explain why an organism has a certain feature, you look to its evolutionary history and the survival advantage that this feature gave the organism. This was the most enlightening aspect of Darwin's theory: that there was a *natural* explanation for the apparent clever design of nature. The reason why bees could cooperate with flowers in pollinating them; the reason why moles have eyes covered with skin; the reason why there are so many things in nature that fit so well together and make such good sense, is not because they were designed that way by a clever God, but because other organisms not so well adapted did not reproduce. In other words, to explain a feature, one must consider the path by which that feature was honed by natural selection.

This is another area, however, in which we find a rough trans-Atlantic divide. The British, generally held to be ultra-Darwinians, claim a major role for natural selection within Darwinism. It is the strategy to explain features of organisms. Gould, Lewontin and other American evolutionists oppose this violently, claiming that there are many features of organisms which *cannot* be explained by natural selection. There may be traits which are present despite not having any survival value. The information about rate of change of environment doesn't seem to fit with the information available about rate of change of species; the environment changes a lot more often although speciation and radical change happen in bursts.

Gould had studied under Dobzhansky, Ernst Mayr, and George Simpson, the leaders of the modern synthesis. He emerged a philosophically committed adaptationist, hoping to supply the quantitative rigour that adaptationist 'story-telling' lacked. However Gould's ideas began to change fairly early in his career. He worked with others just to see if purely random models could encompass the observed order of the fossil record (they could to a surprising degree). The order of the fossil record had been taken as *prima facie* evidence for adaptation. Gould began to change his mind and began to regard adaptationism as a conceptual impediment to evolutionary biology. But he faced the objection of people just not hearing the objection, because 'we know that all well-designed parts of organisms are adaptations'. The point he made was that they may not be.

Gould and his colleague Eldredge attempted to dethrone Darwinism as the central theory of biology by the theory of Punctuation. They claimed that, at the very least, species often showed millions of years of stasis punctuated by relatively brief periods of evolutionary change and speciation. More controversially than that, they also claimed that therefore large-scale change or speciation did *not* take place according to the modern synthesis (accumulation of changes in populations and geographical speciation) but through some other process. In other words, Darwin and modern Darwinians were wrong about speciation. This would indeed be a revolution in evolutionary thinking. It is worth putting Gould's argument, explained in many places, in his own words.

"The generally accepted result of natural selection is adaptation", writes Gould.

We must therefore study natural selection primarily from its results—that is, by concentrating on the putative adaptations of organisms. I know of no scientific mechanism other than natural selection with the proven power to build structures of such eminently workable design.

But does all the rest of evolution—all the phenomena or organic diversity, embryological architecture and genetic structure, for example—flow by simple extrapolation from selection's power to create the good design of organisms? Does the force that makes a functional eye also explain why the world houses more than 500,000 species of beetles and fewer than fifty species of priapulid worms? Or why most nucleotides in multicellular creatures do not code for any enzyme or protein involved in the construction of an organism? Or why ruling dinosaurs died and subordinate mammals survived to flourish and, along one oddly contingent pathway, to evolve a creature capable of building cities and understanding natural selection?"

The answer to all these rhetorical questions in Gould's eyes, is, obviously, no.

[S]election cannot suffice as a full explanation for many aspects of evolution, for other types and styles of causes become relevant, or even prevalent, in domains both far above and far below the traditional Darwinian locus of the organism. These other causes are not, as the ultras[8] often claim, the product of thinly veiled attempts to smuggle purpose back into biology. These additional principles are as directionless, non-teleological, and materialistic as natural selection itself— but they operate differently from Darwin's central mechanism.

Gould goes on to list these other principles.

8. 'Ultra-Darwinians'—Gould's name for Dawkins and other adaptationists.

Population genetics has worked out in theory, and validated in practice, an elegant, mathematical account of the large role that neutral, and therefore nonadaptive, changes play in the evolution of nucleotides, or individual units of DNA programs. Eyes may be adaptations, but most substitutions of one nucleotide for another within populations may not be adaptive.

In the most stunning evolutionary discoveries of the past decade, developmental biologists have documented an astonishing "conservation", or close similarity, of basic pathways of development among phyla that have been evolving independently for at least 500 million years, and that seem so different in basic anatomy (insects and vertebrates, for example). The famous homeotic genes of fruit flies—responsible for odd mutations that disturb the order of parts along the main body axis, placing legs, for example, where antennae or mouth parts should be—are also present (and repeated four times on four separate chromosomes) in vertebrates, where they function in effectively the same way. The major developmental pathway for eyes is conserved and mediated by the same gene in squids, flies and vertebrates, though the end products differ substantially (our single-lens eye versus the multiple facets of insects). The same genes regulate the formation of top and bottom surfaces in insects and vertebrates, though with inverted order—as our back, with the spinal cord running above the gut, is anatomically equivalent to an insect's belly, where the main nerve cords run along the bottom surface, with the gut above.

One could argue, I suppose, that these instances of conservation only record adaptation, unchanged through all of life's vicissitudes because their optimality can't be improved. But most biologists feel that such stability acts primarily as a constraint upon the range and potentiality of adaptation, for if organisms of such different function and ecology must build bodies along the same basic pathways, then limitation of possibilities rather than adaptive honing to perfection becomes a dominant theme in evolution. At a minimum, in explaining evolutionary pathways through time, the constraints imposed by history rise to equal prominence with the immediate advantages of adaptation.

My own field of paleontology has strongly challenged the Darwinian premise that life's major transformations can be explained by adding up, through the immensity of geological time, the successive tiny changes produced generation after generation by natural selection. The extended stability of most species, and the branching off of new species in geological moments (however slow by the irrelevant scale of a human life)—the pattern known as punctuated equilibrium—require that long-term, evolutionary trends be explained as the distinctive success of some species versus others, and not as a gradual accumulation of adaptations generated by organisms within a continuously evolving population. A trend may be set by high rates of branching in certain species within a larger group. But individual organisms do not branch; only populations do—and the causes of a population's branching can rarely be reduced to the adaptive improvement of its individual organisms.

The study of mass extinction has also disturbed the ultra-Darwinian consensus. We now know, at least for the terminal Cretaceous event some sixty-five million years ago which wiped out dinosaurs along with about 50 percent of marine invertebrate species, that some episodes of mass extinction are both truly catastrophic and triggered by extraterrestrial impact. The death of some groups (like dinosaurs) in mass extinctions and the survival or others (like mammals), while surely not random, probably bears little relationship to the evolved, adaptive reasons for successes of lineages in normal Darwinian times dominated by competition. Perhaps mammals survived (and humans ultimately evolved) because small creatures are more resistant to catastrophic extinction. And perhaps Cretaceous mammals were small primarily because they could not compete successfully in the larger size ranges of dominant dinosaurs. Immediate adaptation may bear no relationship to success over immensely long periods of geological change.[9]

In other words, the traditional—and current popular—understanding of evolution, as "…variation proposes and selection disposes"[10] cannot be true. It may be part of the story, Gould acknowledges, but it cannot explain the development of life on earth. If evolution is how we got here, it is not the standard kind of evolution by natural selection which we are taught to revere as our cause. Diversity of species is not necessarily a result of natural selection. It could be because of all sorts of contingent events.

Gould has not been the only vehement opponent of adaptationism. Richard Lewontin, a Harvard colleague of Gould's for some time, took issue in particular with the idea that aspects of morphology, physiology and behaviour of organisms are adaptive *optimal* solutions to problems. He complained that adaptation and optimality are assumed, so that Darwinian research merely aims to explain and exemplify *how* organisms solve problems optimally, not to test *if* they do. We can never be sure, he claimed, that an adaptationist

9.   Stephen Jay Gould, 'More things in heaven and earth', in Hilary Rose and Steven Rose (eds), *Alas, Poor Darwin: Arguments Against Evolutionary Psychology*, Harmony Books, New York, 2000, pp. 101-126, p. 105.
10.   *Ibid.*, p. 110.

explanation of a phenomenon actually happened. Neither can we prove that an observed trait of a species is optimal. Evolution by natural selection destroys the genetic variation on which it feeds, so observation cannot disprove an hypothesis of past evolution.

Lewontin had been convinced by the data that natural selection does not, in fact, lead to the optimal organism in an existing environment. The genetic variability in natural populations turned out to be much greater than evolutionists had believed possible while working on the model of a small reservoir of genetic variation created by mutation and then tested by natural selection. Also, sometimes this variability served no obvious fitness function. As he explained:

> Not all evolutionary change can be understood in terms of adaptation. First, some changes will occur directly by natural selection that are not adaptive...Second, many changes occur indirectly as the result of allometry, or differential growth. The rates of growth of different parts of an organism are different, so that large organisms do not have all their parts in the same proportion. This allometry shows up both between individuals of the same species. Among primate species the brain increases in size more slowly than the body; small apes have a proportionately larger brain than large apes. Since the differential growth is constant for all apes, it is useless to seek an adaptive reason for gorillas having a relatively smaller brain than, say, chimpanzees.
>
> Third, there is the phenomenon of pleiotropy. Changes in a gene have many different effects on the physiology and development of an organism. Natural selection may operate to increase the frequency of the gene because of one of the effects, with pleiotropic, or unrelated, effects being simply carried along. For example, an enzyme that helps to detoxify poisonous substances by converting them into an insoluble

pigment will be selected for its detoxification properties. As a result the colour of the organism will change, but no adaptive explanation of the colour *per se* is either required or correct.

Fourth, many evolutionary changes may be adaptive and yet the resulting differences among species in the character may not be adaptive; they may simply be alternative solutions to the same problem. The theory of population genetics predicts that if more than one gene influences a character, there may often be several alternative stable equilibriums of genetic composition even when the force of natural selection remains the same. Which of these adaptive peaks in the space of genetic composition is eventually reached by a population depends entirely on chance events at the beginning of the selective process...

Finally, many changes in evolution are likely to be purely random. At the present time population geneticists are sharply divided over how much of the evolution of enzymes and other molecules has been in response to natural selection and how much has resulted from the chance accumulation of mutations. It has proved remarkably difficult to get compelling evidence for changes in enzymes brought about by selection, not to speak of evidence for adaptive changes; the weight of evidence at present is that a good deal of amino acid substitution in evolution has been the result of the random fixation of mutations in small populations.[11]

To what extent have Gould, Eldredge and Lewontin convinced their colleagues? Not greatly, it seems. Many evolutionists contend that the whole issue is hardly important. Maynard Smith, for instance, has not taken the punctuated evolutionists arguments very seriously. "A change taking 50 000 years is sudden to a paleontologist but gradual to a population geneticist...my

11.   R. C. Lewontin, 'Adaptation', *Scientific American*, 1978, *239*, pp. 156-69, pp. 167-8.

guess is that there is not much more to the argument than that." After all, it is not as if the punctuationists have a new theory to replace Darwinism. "Perhaps the greatest weakness of the punctuationists is their failure to suggest a plausible alternative mechanism."[12]

From the first presentation of objections to adaptationism in 1978, Richard Dawkins has generally dismissed the arguments as either irrelevant or missing the point. Most of the time, he claims, he and his colleagues have simply been misrepresented. "Bitter experience warns that a biologist who shows a strong interest in functional explanation is likely to be accused, sometimes with a passion that startles those more accustomed to scientific than ideological debate, of believing that all animals are perfectly optimal—accused of being an 'adaptationist'."[13] As you may gather, Dawkins considers this 'accusation' an exaggerated and inapplicable one, in particular inapplicable to himself. No one, he says, is an extreme adaptationist as Gould and Lewontin portray them; and anyway, common-sense adaptationism is a very strong position. Adaptationism has been a fruitful working hypothesis over the years as seemingly unimportant features turned out to be adaptive after all.

> Adaptationist thinking, if not blind conviction, has been a valuable stimulator of testable hypotheses in physiology... cautious adaptationist reasoning can suggest which of many possible physiological hypotheses are most promising and should be tested first.[14]

Dawkins acknowledges there are some constraints on natural

12. Quoted in Segestrom, *op, cit.*, p. 126.
13. Dawkins, *Extended Phenotype, op. cit.*, p. 30.
14. *Ibid.*, p. 32.

selection to optimal adaptation, but that these are hardly critical, and some of the suggested problems are not relevant at all. Dawkins deals just as dismissively with other objections raised by Gould. Each opponent is thoroughly convinced of his position, and it seems unlikely that any accord will be reached. There is a fundamental divide between the views of these two men, and no common ground of agreement, or even real discussion, seems to be possible.

⊰9⊱

DARWINISM TODAY

At the beginning of this book, we saw an explanation of evolutionary theory, in clear language, concise format, and easily understood. It is a straightforward theory, with straightforward evidence. Darwin made the revolutionary breakthrough, and it has all been plain sailing since then.

Except, of course, for the times when it has not. Darwin's significant idea, brilliant as it was, has been added to, expanded upon, and recast until it is almost unrecognisable. The underlying theories of genetics and inheritance have been through major revolutions and are still uncovering vast areas of our ignorance. Moreover, even the basic statement of what the shape of evolutionary theory should be is a matter of strong contention. Disagreement extends to the very meaning of the term 'Darwinian', and arguments range from minute detail to sweeping theories covering millennia.

These arguments have claimed slabs of column space in academic and popular publications all over the world. That merely makes them the most prominent controversy; but there are other objections to the Darwinian status quo altogether. Biologist Lynn Margulis, for instance, opposes the essential premise of selection based on competition, and insists that mutation is not a sufficient source of variation for natural selection to act. Instead, she has developed a view of evolution by cooperative means. "We consider naïve the early Darwinian view of 'nature red in tooth and claw'", she has written. "Now we see ourselves as products of cellular cooperation—of cells built up from other cells. Partnerships between cells once foreign and even enemies to each other are at the very roots of our being. They are the basis of the continually outward expansion of life on Earth."[15] Although Margulis has had some astounding predictive successes with her views on cellular biology, her wider views on the mode of evolution are generally dismissed.

Other problems exist within different areas of evolutionary theory; the continuing problem of scientific fraud associated with the extremely lucrative business of fossil-trading; public conflict over dating of fossils and rock layers; and ongoing feuds such as that surrounding the Leakey family in Kenya.

We must remember that there are thousands of evolutionary biologists doing careful, honest and intelligent work. Their work should not be denigrated just because there are controversies raging on a different level.

However, the fact that thousands of biologists do good work on the basis of evolutionary theory does not change the fact that there *are* extensive controversies within the current field of evolutionary biology. These do not make the theory wrong; but they do demonstrate that evolutionary theory is not the monolithic, unassailable 'fact' so often presented in science literature.

It is no answer to contend that these debates are about the *mechanism* of evolution, not evolution itself; for it is the very explanatory power of the mechanism of natural selection that makes evolutionary theory compelling. An insistence on evolution *without* mechanism is a rather empty idea. We have various things to explain: the fossil record, the similarities between different species on a physiological and genetic level, the geographical distribution of species. A theory of descent

15. Lynn Margulis, *Early Life*, Science Books International, Boston, 1982, p. 138.

with modification would, indeed, provide that explanation; but we do not have such a theory except in speculation. Natural selection does not appear convincingly to account for all features which look well-designed, or for the origin of species. To say for the rest 'it just happened'—even if you call this 'the importance of contingent events'—is not a strong theory. We may as well have stuck with 'That's the way God did it'. The rhetoric on behalf of evolutionary theory—'evolution is a fact'—is misleading as long as there are major areas in which it fails to provide explanation for the living world as we see it today, and there is considerable dispute amongst biologists as to what proper evolutionary reasoning is at all.

Nonetheless, these bitter disputes disappear when evolutionary theory puts on a public face. "Virtually all thinking people accept the factuality of evolution and no conclusion in science enjoys better documentation."[16] If all living organisms are descended from an initial organism, that would explain things such as the similarities in genetic structure between the different 'branches' of animals. There is, indeed, a family resemblance between different species. Yet this has become an article of faith, that *only* this theory can explain the world around us—that it is not even a theory, but a fact. This combines with other articles of faith: that the fossil record demonstrates descent with modification, that the mechanism is natural selection (with quibbles about how powerful it is). The public face of evolution, particularly when it confronts religion, is solidarity in absolute, proven truth. Part of this problem is a matter of definition (what kind of 'evolution' is being spoken of?) and part is the problem of simplification, as

16. Stephen Jay Gould, in Rose and Rose, *op. cit.*, p. 103.

we have already discussed—but a lot of the exaggerated claims about evolutionary theory display a heartfelt, deeply held faith in its truth regardless of problems.

Yet some questions remain. If Gould is right—if indeed there are aspects of apparent design *not* explained by natural selection—then has not Darwin's alternative to natural theology failed? If the reason that Darwinism was so successful was that he "made it possible to be an intellectually fulfilled atheist",[17] then atheists may have to admit they are not so intellectually fulfilled after all. Yet such a question would *never* receive sensible discussion within the evolutionary community.

Why is Darwinism still so tenaciously atheist? Why is the only opposition seen as coming from creationism when between evolutionists there are such bitter battles? If evolutionary theory is, in the end, a matter of evidence and scientific reasoning, why can we never seem to have an open, scientific discussion of the different aspects of evolutionary theory? The answer that seems to be implicit in many atheist replies is that creation scientists keep the religious politics going by their attacks on science. But really, one could make the same accusation of prominent evolutionists themselves, who appear to pounce on religion at any public opportunity. Are evolutionists really so hostage to religious believers—as if without the believers, all the controversy would go away? Why is evolution so religious?

17. Richard Dawkins, *The Blind Watchmaker*, Penguin Books, London, 1986, p. 6.

Part III

DARWINISM AND RELIGION

No matter how hard you try to discuss evolutionary theory impartially and dispassionately, someone's ideology always seems to take over the debate. Creationists accuse evolutionists of propagating their religion of secular humanism; evolutionists accuse creationists of hijacking science in the name of religious fundamentalism. Everyone tries to present their case on the scientific evidence alone, but the fights over ideology are always there.

The problem is that try as we might to make evolutionary theory neutral, it never has been. It is standard to talk of 'this is the science, the facts' and 'these are religious implications that people add to the facts'. But that assumes that there is or ever has been a neutral, context-free theory; particularly a religiously neutral theory. There never has been. From the first detailed evolutionary theory to the present, evolution has always been an idea firmly embedded in a religious—or, more often, anti-religious—framework.

This is not just a matter of saying that the English society in which Darwin wrote was one dominated by the Anglican church. In many ways it was—and this certainly influenced the theory's reception—but even more than that, the very idea of evolution has always been imbued with religious and social politics.[1]

To demonstrate this, we will go back to some of the early evolutionary theories, before Charles Darwin and his natural selection appeared on the scene.

1. Of course, it can be argued that every scientific theory always has been. But in evolution, this is both more blatant and more vehemently denied than in other theories.

⊷ 10 ⊷
EVOLUTION BEFORE CHARLES DARWIN

To get a taste of evolutionary flavour before Charles Darwin, we need first to go back two generations.

Erasmus Darwin

One of the first evolutionary theories may be said to have been developed by Erasmus Darwin, Charles' grandfather, although to call it a 'theory' may be a little grandiose. Erasmus believed in the transmutation of species—that is, that one species can develop or 'transmute' into another species. This belief was based on his study of fossils and because of homology—the similarities between different species. He supported the idea of inheritance of acquired characteristics, some ten years before Lamarck, in his treatise *Zoonomia* (1794). This was actually a medical treatise, with not much by way of detail or even rigour, but it did spell out a big, sweeping idea of evolution. He was trying to make sense of the facts of nature as he saw them, but there was not much of a scientific theory there.

Erasmus was not a Christian—at most he was a Deist, believing in a creator God, but one not interested in the continued running of the world. Erasmus believed in the existence of unbroken natural law set up by God at the beginning, and his ideas on evolution suited this, if not explicitly driven by it. His England was the home of the industrial revolution. The idea of the world as a perfect machine needing no intervention after it was set running was a powerful one. Indeed, the industrial metaphor was central to Erasmus Darwin's thinking. He also held a philosophy of life that saw the future in the prosperous middle class—science-loving, democratic, rationalist and urban. Part and parcel of this philosophy was a belief in a progressive, ever-improving, natural evolution.

Then, as now, the things that counted in good science were predictive accuracy, coherence, consistency, unificatory power, fertility and simplicity. Judged by these, Erasmus' theory was regarded as hardly scientific. It did not involve experiment or systematic study of nature, there was no effort at genuine integration with known science, and no prediction; it was more a string of anecdotes and curious facts. In any case, he wrote most of it in poetry, which (as now) was no way to do serious science. What Erasmus presented was evolution as part of a world picture which described his philosophy. His most serious critics were not scientists but those who opposed the philosophy, such as those sickened by the French Revolution, which Darwin had initially supported and which also proclaimed such progressive evolutionary ideas. Erasmus was ridiculed and rejected. People did not want a progressivist philosophy that ended in the guillotine.

French theorists and revolutionaries

Erasmus Darwin was an eccentric, whose views—although prophetic given his later family history—were not taken terribly seriously. Nineteenth-century biologists before Charles Darwin generally held that species cannot be turned into other species. This 'neoclassical' biology was a successful theory, drawing on classical sources such as Aristotle but with a modern framework.

It was a holistic theory, holding that the organism is a whole, tightly interlinked and interdependent. When Darwin mentions 'the mysterious correlation of parts' that is a problem for his theory, he is probably referring to this idea.

The idea of the fortuitous fit of parts was held to go along with a drive to reproduce, which propagates more of the same. Any variations in offspring were held to be merely oscillations around a norm. As experience could show, too much variation and you get a monster which does not reproduce. Animals are perfectly adapted to their environment because they are reproduced faithfully.

The French biologist Cuvier was a major proponent of this view. He divided organisms into four basic groupings, or embranchments, and held that there could be no passage between embranchments. This, however, could not account for the appearance of new animal groups in the fossil record, so Cuvier held all the more strongly to separate creation. To adhere to a Christian idea, however, was abhorrent to his less conservative colleagues. The French Revolution of 1789 had stimulated a break with neoclassicism in general—the Revolution was explicitly known to be connected with evolutionary science. Lamarck, who held to the politics of the French Revolution and the overthrow of the church, considered Cuvier's belief in creation irrational. Lamarck therefore opposed his theory, deciding that embranchments were not impassable after all. Lamarck and his colleague Saint-Hilaire also challenged the fixity of species as held by scientists whom they identified with the old regime. This is precisely what the first fully worked out evolutionary theory was about; a consequence of political opposition to creationism, rather than something developed on its own merits.

In meeting such challenges, however, comparative anatomists such as Cuvier and Owen, and the embryologist von Baer, succeeded in breathing new life into neoclassicism. Charles Darwin, therefore, was quite on the defensive. The burden of proof fell on the evolutionists, who were required to show that it could happen, contrary to common sense. It was important, therefore, for Lamarck—and Charles Darwin—to provide a mechanism by which new species could develop from existing forms.

Lamarck proposed evolution by inheritance of acquired characteristics, as we have discussed earlier. He suggested that all of life was descended from several starting points. His theory was completely atheist. Other biologists had variations on the theme; those with a materialist bent made the theory popular with revolutionaries. Cuvier was appalled, as evolutionary theory was a challenge to the fundamental assumptions of neoclassical biology. He fought, and won, the public battle against certain evolutionary theorists, but in the process made Lamarck more famous, and associated evolution in general with progressive French culture. When *The Origin of Species* was translated into French, it was introduced as support for Lamarckian evolution, as well as for political progressivism, materialism and anticlericalism.

In other words, the evolutionary theory was hardly promoted for its scientific merits, at least initially. The differences between Lamarckianism and Darwinism were not even clearly understood. The scientific arguments and evidence for (or against) evolutionary theory were, frankly, a minor consideration. Far more important in the social context were the anti-Christian propaganda opportunities evolutionary theory provided. It was not an explanation so much as a weapon.

But what of Darwin himself? We have often heard the story of the young man who at one stage was studying to be an Anglican minister before his trip on the *Beagle* started him thinking about natural selection. We know through numerous reports and biographies that although he gradually lost his religious belief over the years, he never made this public or engaged in anti-Christian debate. This was probably out of respect for his devoutly Christian wife as much as not being inclined to cause controversy. So, then, surely his theory was truly a scientific breakthrough based on his long and painstaking research, and not at all part of anti-Christian propaganda?

As we shall see, the story is never as simple as that.

=11=

CHARLES DARWIN'S BACKGROUND

Charles Darwin developed his theory in a country facing unprecedented turmoil in economics, philosophy, social organisation and religion. Science was inevitably both affected by and used in service of various competing factions. Although part of the very fight was to create the image of science as impartial, objective and authoritative, scientific theories were nonetheless philosophical weapons as much as they were reasoned ideas about nature.

Indeed, nature itself was subject to philosophical change in the nineteenth century. The young Darwin was exposed to and affected by the fervent passion about nature's way, nourished by Romantic poetry, especially Wordsworth and the Romantic reading of Milton. Darwin's earliest view of science was a Romantic one—as a high calling, a noble pursuit. He read Humboldt's *Personal Narrative* at Cambridge and said it gave him "a burning zeal to add even the most humble contribution to the noble structure of natural science".[2] This was a view of science as a process of acquiring knowledge through identification with nature, an almost mystical trip into the sublime inner life of the world.

England, meanwhile, was in turmoil. The 1830 Reform Bill gave greater political representation to the middle classes, who were also pressing for greater access to professions like law, medicine and education, and more market-oriented economic policies. The First Reform Bill increased the economic,

2. N. Barlow (ed.), *The Autobiography of Charles Darwin*, Collins, London, 1958, p. 67.

social and political power of the professional and mercantile middle class without, however, improving the lot of industrial workers or the urban and rural poor.

England was also heading for a major change in religious philosophy. By the end of the nineteenth century, the country had seen "the turning of the balance of educated intelligence from the current creed to unbelief".[3] The groundbreaking *Essays and Reviews* had been published in 1860, describing new inquiries (now discredited) into the historicity of the Bible. Two of the authors were tried in church courts for heresy and saved from conviction only by appeal to the Privy Council.

Outward piety was still strong throughout the century: chapels and churches remained crowded, books of sermons were best-sellers, missionary zeal was high, and itinerant preachers such as Moody and Sankey pursued wildly successful evangelism. However the proportion of churchgoers compared to population was dropping, and orthodoxy—quite possibly overly complacent after centuries of authority—was being thrown on the unfamiliar defensive. At the same time, several public and literary figures turned away from the faith with loud cries of disillusionment. The anguish of loss of belief may have been a pose, of course; many gladly embraced the new perversity and decadence, such as Oscar Wilde, Aubrey Beardsley and Ernest Dowson. Mental anguish and the death of illusions for the sake of mankind merely gave a romantic tinge to such 'sacrifice'. Moreover, "[I]t appeared that the more dismal was one's belief the more painful was the parting from it".[4] Then there

---

3. John McKinnon Robertson, *History of Freethought in the Nineteenth Century*, London, 1929, quoted in Warren Sylvester Smith, *The London Heretics 1870-1914*, Constable, London, 1967, p. 2.
4. Smith, *ibid.*, p. 5.

would appear a great sense of liberation and energy. "Indeed the entire period must owe much to these early repressions as the source of its later unparalleled vitality".[5] Noted authors Beatrix Potter and George Eliot both displayed a conversion from a highly repressive and stunted form of Christianity to a relieved and relaxed apostasy. The loss of belief, or the struggle to retain it, was the theme of many poems and stories, such as William Hale White's *The Autobiography of Mark Rutherford* and *Mark Rutherford's Deliverance*, and *Robert Elsmere* by Mrs Humphry Ward.

With the rise of industry, England also began to experience a social blight of a scale and kind previously unknown. Information on poverty was slow to spread and badly received, but as the century wore it became increasingly clear that the profits of industry had failed millions of Britons. Children were kept drugged in order to keep them working appallingly long hours; infant mortality was extremely high amongst the poor, as underfed mothers were forced to keep up factory work; vast numbers of working-class families lived well below subsistence level. There were some social improvements by the end of the century—free compulsory education, reform legislation, public health and factory laws, paving and sewerage, housing regulations—but for most of the nineteenth century, London saw horrible poverty, "sodden with drink" as General Booth, the founder of the Salvation Army, put it.

The guilty horror that occurred among the more fortunate as these conditions received more publicity created a wide range of social reform movements. The first impulse of the wealthy was charity, but often the reform movement rejected it, as charity would never be sufficient. The new groups of socialists

5. *Ibid.*, p. 6.

denounced charity as counter-revolutionary and immoral, looking for a more general re-arrangement of society. Socialism took many forms, some of them religious; there were also secular socialists and secular anti-socialists. Fabians preached equalisation of income, and Marxists revolution.

There arose, no doubt fostered by carefully targeted propaganda, a faith in science for social improvement. At the same time, Christianity was associated with conservatism and the old order which had created the problems—an attitude not helped by conservatives whose Christianity was far more a matter of traditional privilege than it was of belief. Some Christian groups dedicated to improving society were frowned on by traditionalists as materialists. Many groups were vehemently anti-Christian. Winwood Reade in *The Martyrdom of Man* claimed that supernatural Christianity was false, while science would bring improved transport and improved food manufacture. He also predicted moral improvement and social advances along with the scientific, for when man had conquered the outer world, he would subdue the inner evil. (How naïve this appears to twenty-first century readers!)

There were many social reformers who were outright, and outspoken, heretics. Many reforms, too, were very successful; laws were introduced for improvement in education, trade unions, public health, workmen's housing, dangerous occupations, factory conditions, local government, tenants' rights, land purchase, public finance, and so on. But they also aimed to change minds. And they did, often succeeding in having reform associated with heterodoxy. Although orthodox Christians achieved great social reforms—such as abolition of slavery, rescue of women and children from sex-slavery and prostitution, and improvements in women's conditions—the secularist reforms achieved far more publicity.

Secularism was growing, helped by the fact that the Anglican church was largely staffed by younger sons interested mainly in a secure living. Clear understanding of the Bible, and intellectual rigour in expounding it, was not common. Anglicanism had to a large extent settled into a comfortable, polite institution, with immense social power. It is hardly surprising that secular intellectuals resented the position of this institution, whose philosophy they disagreed with. They wanted the power to be linked with their own point of view. The social milieu was changing, and social Christianity—which made up a good proportion of the church—was losing ground.

⊷ 12 ⊷

DARWIN, THE GENTLEMAN EVOLUTIONIST

Into this world came Charles Darwin, a respectable and educated man, with an allowance from his father, as well as inherited parts of the Wedgewood fortune through his mother and wife. On his return from the famous voyage on the *Beagle*, Darwin was in the perfect position to engage in scientific activity like a gentleman. He enlisted several colleagues to help him catalogue his specimens from the voyage. He was asked to join the prestigious Geological Society (as well as the Linnean and Zoological societies). He published learned papers on geology, and in 1839 published *The Voyage of the Beagle*, a popular success. Darwin was made a member of the Royal Society and moved to a large country house. He served as vestryman of the local Anglican church and was a close friend of the rector. He was a picture of the traditional, privileged, Anglican gentleman.

He held a shameful secret, however—like the French revolutionaries, enemies of church and monarchist orthodoxy, he was inclined to think that species *were not fixed*. Darwin had to conceal his transmutationist ideas. He was secretary of the Geological Society, and would certainly have been dismissed had his ideas been known. Even Lyell, the geologist whose work had considerably increased estimates of the age of the world into millennia, denied transmutation with horror. He held, as most scientists did, to a basically fixed history of biology, with the occasional extinction and special creation of new forms. Evolution, Lyell believed, would degrade human reason to the level of an ape.

At the same time Darwin socialised with the philosophical liberals. His brother Erasmus was going out with Harriet Martineau, a prominent writer for the *Westminster Review,* and their circle included George Eliot, George Lewes, Thomas Carlyle, and later Herbert Spencer, John Stuart Mill and Harriet Taylor. In their presence he would have heard ideas of social reform associated with heterodox religious notions and mildly revolutionary political ideas. At that time, however, evolution was socialist and only discussed by those in sympathy with the working class, which Darwin did not want. It would take him into the circles of the outright revolutionaries, far beyond the polite apostasy of the literary liberals.

Darwin's adherence to evolution and common descent was therefore a problem for him. The only theory of a mechanism for evolution was that of Lamarck and Geoffroy, who were both considered heretical. Privately, Darwin may have been more willing to take on such ideas than some of his conservative colleagues. Darwin's own family had had a few colourful characters. His freethinking and sexually freewheeling grandfather Erasmus Darwin was, after all, rather radical about matter and sensation in the neopagan era before the French Revolution. His book *Zoonomia,* as well as giving evolutionary ideas, also celebrated sexual pleasure and relief from religious orthodoxy. Darwin could not publicly identify with his grandfather in his time, but the influences were there privately.

It was clear, however, that if Darwin were to announce publicly a theory of evolution, it could not be Lamarckian. It would to have to be solidly British, in the best tradition of established science. It would still be socially risky, which no doubt contributed to Darwin's delay in publishing. While his diaries show that he held evolutionary ideas from 1837, he did not describe them to close friends until 1856, when he invited some scientific peers to his house for a meeting. T. H. Huxley, the atheist who was to become 'Darwin's Bulldog', fighting for science to oust the church as a social authority, was there. Thomas Verson Wollaston, an entomologist who had written on the great range of variation in insect species, was also invited, but he went away shocked. So did Lyell, who thought that no matter how much variation a species could tolerate there were essentialist limits to it. While Huxley doubted the power of natural selection to produce new species, he championed the theory because of its anti-theism. Lyell, on the other hand, thought that the theory well might be correct and hated it—because of its anti-theism.

Initially, Darwin's theory attracted little comment, but as it became more famous, its anti-Christian implications were felt. Darwin himself remained unobtrusively Anglican, despite his private thoughts, but had no objection to promoters such as Huxley using his theory to attack Christianity. Most churchmen were, understandably enough, initially quite resistant— especially considering the understood scientific deficiencies of the idea.

In understanding the religious controversy at the time, we need to see the way in which Christianity as a philosophy, and the church as a social power, had become confused, even by many genuine believers. The church as an institution was interested in maintaining its power. Many of its officials were only dubiously Christian, holding more to a theistic conservatism than actual Christianity. Defending the 39 Articles and the social authority of the church was all important. The famous controversy of the Oxford Movement, in which several leading churchmen 'defected' to Catholicism, was essentially over this issue—the Church of England could not be the true church, these men ultimately decided, for some key court cases proved that the state had ultimate authority over the church. Only the Roman church, which did not have such restrictions, could be the true church. This view, although having little to do with biblical Christianity, shaped much of church politics during the century.

Such church leaders saw Darwinism as a threat—as indeed it was, with Huxley and his colleagues behind it. The anti-church lobby took up Darwinism as a tool against the church. In this they were helped by the fact that the church had allied itself to the natural theology of Paley.

William Paley was a Cambridge theologian who in 1802 had published *Natural Theology, or Evidences of the Existence and attributes of the Deity.* It followed in a long tradition of eighteenth-century defences of Christianity on the basis of natural evidence and reason. Paley's book in particular became hugely popular, and was probably read by most schoolboys and university students in the country throughout the nineteenth century. It became a standard reference for the rationality of Christianity. Its chief argument was from design—that is, arguing that the world must have been designed by a rational being, because the world shows so much evidence of well-designed systems.

It is an old argument, but Paley's triumph was in giving a wealth of examples, utilising the latest scientific discoveries and going into fascinating detail. He concentrated particularly on the way in which the different parts of an organism, or different organisms in proximity with each other, work together so beautifully. You would naturally assume, Paley wrote, if you found a watch, never having seen one before, that it was deliberately designed, because all the cogs and wheels fit together so efficiently in such intricate detail. Only something crafted by a master could possibly have so many interacting parts that work so well. In the same way, Paley's book went on to describe, when you look at the incredible intricacy of the natural world, the workings of the eye or the process of pollinating a flower, you have to conclude that the natural world has a designer. The world itself is testimony to a creator God.

This was an explanation of the world which Darwin specifically challenged. Yes, he agreed, the way in which nature works, each part fitting so well with another, is indeed marvellous. But we do not need to assert deliberate craftsmanship to explain it. No, Darwin said, the reason that all these organisms work so well together is because the ones who did not work so well did not survive. Nature itself has selected out the successful elements of its machinery. This did not mean that there was no Creator—Darwin himself postulated a Creator to begin the process with the initial organism(s)— but it did undercut Paley's argument for the existence of a Creator. The fact that there are plenty of other reasons to believe in a Creator was not prominent in the ensuing publicity. The Church of England had depended on the argument of Paley's *Natural Theology* for its intellectual basis, and that argument had just been substantially undermined.

Once again the church had allied itself to a particular stripe of science, and when the science was challenged, saw its power threatened. Just as the medieval church had suffered when its allegiance to Aristotelian cosmology was challenged by Galileo's Copernican cosmology, the Anglican church was shaken by its wholesale endorsement of a particular understanding of the workings of nature.

Darwin may well have been driven to his theory by intellectual reasons and the weight of evidence, but there is no particular reason that it had to be presented in such an atmosphere of anti-Christianity. This was due to a number of factors: it was because French evolutionists set up their theory as part of their anti-establishment, anti-church revolutionist philosophy; it was because atheists like Huxley wanted a political tool against the church, and Darwin, respectable gentleman that he was, yet had a radical background and youth and was quite happy to let them use his theory; and it was because the church in its political arrogance and theological laziness, had latched onto anti-evolutionary biology as the bulwark of its beliefs and therefore authority.

If none of these conditions had been present, would evolution ever have been seen as an enemy of Christianity, by believers or atheists? Maybe not—but we can hardly judge, for if it had not been such a charged political issue, Darwin's theory may well have mouldered in scientific libraries for years, and whatever theory of historical biology we now had may have been entirely different. Take the religious politics out of Darwinism and you have none of the intense interest poured into it not just at the beginning, but ever since. Darwinism has never been examined outside a context of attacks on the political and intellectual status of the Christian church.

⊷13⊷
THE SYNTHESISERS

As Darwinism entered the twentieth century, its scientific foundations may have been a little shaky (as we saw in the first section), but its role in religious arguments was thriving. There were always those who accepted Darwinistic evolution as a possible, even likely, method of God's creation, but this view was firmly opposed by political atheists. It suited the atheist camp to cast evolution as the downfall of Christianity, especially as the theory began to gain scientific ground as the new century progressed.

Flamboyantly positive atheists have been prominent amongst evolutionary theorists of the twentieth century. J. B. S. Haldane, for instance, combined a career of high-profile evolutionary science with outspoken reductionist material-ism—the view that there is no supernatural existence whatsoever. Haldane was a tough character with a public school background, who found he liked killing German soldiers and was very good at it. His materialism meant he had no scruples about this: war was a natural feature of human society. He despised the Christian God and the do-gooder ethics. He was attracted to communism not because of any love of the working class, but out of an aristocratic contempt for the bourgeoisie, and an attraction to the idea of a scientifically planned society and shared atheism.[6]

6.   Taken from David J. Depew and Bruce H. Weber, *Darwinism Evolving: Systems Dynamics and the Genelogy of Natural Selection,* The MIT Press, Cambridge, Mass. and London, England, 1986, pp. 235-7.

However not all the religious ideology surrounding evolutionary theory has been atheist. Although it is less usual, some prominent evolutionary theorists have seen their science within a theistic framework, although not a mainstream Christian one, and they have tended to keep the two subjects separate in their public writings. Fisher's population genetics, for instance, was for him part of a grand metaphysical scheme, which involved a peculiar combination of Christian ideas and a passion for positive eugenics. Evolution kept moving up, he believed, to higher forms of life, reaching humans, and giving improved cultural forms. There it tended to go backwards, however, because the people at the top tended to restrict their breeding. Eugenics must therefore be set up to encourage the upper classes to reproduce more. These social views echoed, and perhaps influenced, his evolutionary theory. Selection in his theory moves organisms slowly up to a peak of fitness, as we have seen, in an inexorable way similar to the second law of thermodynamics.

George Price, who was later to develop important ideas in the mathematics of kin selection, also combined a type of Christianity with his evolutionary theory. For him, however, it was a totally depressive combination (although he appears to have had a depressive mental illness as well). His deep involvement in poor relief left him a financial and physical wreck, and his own mathematics which analysed altruism in terms of selfish survival tactics led him to despair and, eventually, suicide. For Price, the religious and ethical implications of evolution seemed to him so important that his life can be seen to have depended on them.

The Russian-American geneticist Theodosius Dobzhansky was another who saw in evolutionary theory a basis for progressive theistic ideas. His work was very influential, and moved the whole field of evolutionary biology up a notch in academic rigour. His predictive claims about variations in a population were experimentally triumphant. Dobzhansky went into evolution with a mission to show that the deity is working his purpose in the evolutionary realm, and that man is his finest creation in upward progression. In America he turned to the process-theological thought of Bergson and Whitehead, and later Teilhard de Chardin, who combined an idea of spiritual evolution of the universe with natural evolution. Dobzhansky developed a kind of pan-Christianity, and openly said that if his science did not underpin his progressionism he would like science less.

Dobzhansky's later writings contain much about freedom, morality and religion. However no matter how overt his ideology was in his general thinking, he took care not to combine it officially with his science. Dobzhansky had two quite distinct sets of writing: scientific books and articles, and popular articles for the nonscientific reader in which he explained his ideology. In this way he felt he could be true to science and himself.[7]

Evolution in the first half of the twentieth century had reached previously unknown heights of scientific respectability. It had come to earn its place as an acknowledged academic discipline with the rigour and seriousness expected of the sciences. It was also more than ever associated with overtones of religious controversy. We will now look at some of the more famous events in that controversy.

It is remarkable, though, just how ideologically charged evolutionary theory continued to be. Even as it became an established research discipline, its public and popular face con-

7. See Michael Ruse, *Mystery of Mysteries: Is Evolution a Social Construction?*, Harvard University Press, Cambridge, Mass. and London, England, 1999, for further details.

tinued to include 'expert' pronouncements on what evolutionary theory meant for God, and vice versa. Indeed, in America at least, staged public events were soon to be used specifically to associate evolution with the highest scientific ideals, and Christianity with anti-science nonsense. If anything, the more scientific evolutionary theory was to become, the more it was used to draw religious, specifically anti-Christian, conclusions.

— 14 —

THE PUBLIC BATTLES
OF THE TWENTIETH CENTURY

We now see the twentieth century as a time of fierce competition between evolution and Christianity. In one sense, this was nothing new: on the public front, evolutionary discourse has been dominated by the atheists from Huxley's time onwards. But the twentieth century has seen battles not just in journals and newspapers, but in courtrooms and government houses, over the religious status of evolutionary theory. Certainly the twentieth century inherited theological battles of the nineteenth century, but why did they continue so vehemently? What drove evolutionists to court?

The blame is generally placed upon the American fundamentalist movement, which early in the century shifted from intelligent appreciation of the possibilities of biological theory to a more embattled defensiveness. Once this had happened, the public image of evolution seemed established as the enemy of Christian belief. This perception was hardly driven by the Christian position, however. Specific attacks on Christianity on the basis of evolution, a public image that meant debates were consistently reported within a framework of 'warfare', and the openly atheist allegiance of prominent evolutionary theorists, meant that the true intellectual issues involved were rarely articulated and even less often understood.

The change in the nature of Christian approaches to evolution, particularly in the more conservative states of America, can be seen in the last years of the nineteenth and early twentieth century. For a long time after Darwin, it is difficult to find clerics who believed in a young earth or a 'six-day' reading of Genesis 1, even when they opposed evolution. The series of booklets called 'The Fundamentals', which gave the Fundamentalist movement its name, presented quite a positive view of evolutionary science in the articles by the theologians B. B. Warfield and James Orr.[8] Despite atheist attacks to the contrary, theologians demonstrated that the ideas of Christianity and a creator God were not essentially opposed to an ancient earth or an evolutionary explanation of the fossil record.

The political attacks on Christianity by materialist thinkers, however, became harder to bear. As the relentless attacks on theism itself continued on the basis of evolution, biblical believers turned to defending the Bible as the issue of primary importance rather than discussing its harmonies with evolution. As a polemical tactic, after all, harmonising the Bible with evolutionary theory was not very successful. Atheist opponents did not really care if it could be done; their attack was on the notion of a Creator God itself rather than on the specifics of biblical detail. In self-defence, then, various Christian groups retreated into a more narrow sphere of debate.

This tendency is exemplified in the career of George Frederick Wright, scientist and cleric. Born in upstate New York, Wright studied theology and followed science as an avid interest. While a pastor in New England, his field studies led him to become a recognized expert on the ice age in New England, and he served as a director of the Boston Society of Natural History. He was offered chairs in biology and geology at various universities, but preferred to stay within the ministry. Wright was no enemy of science; he appreciated and understood the scientific method, and defended evolutionary

8.   See Kirsten Birkett, 'Darwin and the Fundamentalists', *kategoria*, 1996, *2*, pp. 25-53.

and geological theories against anti-scientific Christian groups. As time wore on, however, he apparently became tired of opposing those with whom he essentially agreed on important matters—God, Jesus, the inspiration of the Bible—and defending those who persisted in attacking him on those same issues. From the 1880s on, therefore, he moved from defending evolution to defending the historicity of the Bible. In the process, he moved to a more scientistic reading of Genesis—taking it as a comment on scientific theories of the earth, rather than a theological interpretation of history.

It was a move that other American intellectuals were to make, as they began to perceive a trend towards dissolution and licentiousness amongst the educated level of society, which they attributed in large part to evolutionary teaching. As the twentieth century moved on and associations were made between German aggression and Darwinism, this moral antagonism to the materialistic evolutionary theories continued. Given the evident scientific problems with Darwinism at the time, it is not difficult to understand why a religiously conservative public might reject the need to teach evolutionary theory to children at all. William Jennings Bryant, one-time Secretary of State and fierce advocate of democracy, considered their position a valid one. When an overwhelming majority in the Tennessee House of Representatives passed a bill against teaching "any theory that denies the story of the Divine Creation of man as taught in the Bible, and to teach instead that man had descended from a lower order of animal", Bryant fought for their democratic right to hold such a position.

This is essentially what the "Monkey Trial" in Tennessee was about. The American Civil Liberties Union used this bill, and the hapless teacher John Scopes (who was set up to oppose it), as a test case for their ideas of academic freedom.

The public image of the trial, however, merely reflected the already entrenched notion that any objection to evolution can only be a misguided religious prejudice. Once again, evolution was to be the weapon wielded against Christian belief, rather than an idea to be discussed. The real issues of the trial, and its outcome, were lost beneath an ideological battle.[9]

That ideological battle continues, and the real legal disputes continue to be misrepresented and distorted even in scholarly publications. What has become standard belief is that evolution is atheistic and therefore unchristian, and any who try to dilute this stance are soft in one way or another—soft in the head, or soft on Christian faith. Yet evolutionists continue to write about religion. There is something about evolutionary theory which seems to cry out for a connection with religion. We now turn to a few examples of prominent evolutionists who have made this connection.

9.   For further discussion, see Kirsten Birkett, 'History gone wrong', *kategoria*, 1998, *11*, pp. 47-58.

⊷ 15 ⊷

THREE MODERN RELIGIOUS EVOLUTIONISTS

The ideological connection between evolutionary theory and atheism has continued to this day. Here we will look at three prominent evolutionary theorists who cannot, it seems, ponder on evolution without making certain claims about religion. The way they resolve the relationship between the two areas is very different; but for all three, religious explanations cannot be left behind.

Richard Dawkins: religion, the enemy

> Science shares with religion the claim that it answers deep questions about origins, the nature of life and the cosmos. But there the resemblance ends. Scientific beliefs are supported by evidence, and they get results. Myths and faiths are not and do not.[10]

Richard Dawkins confidently asserts that atheism is true and that this is based on a scientific understanding of the world. Correspondingly, he insists that there is no evidence for religion—by which he most commonly refers to Protestant Christianity. This theme appears in most of his books, but is particularly exemplified in the biblically-titled *River Out of Eden*.

Dawkins not only ignores any evidence asserted in favour of Christianity, but claims to defeat theism in general by

---

10. Richard Dawkins, *River Out of Eden: A Darwinian View of Life*, Weidenfeld and Nicolson, London, 1995, p. 33.

various tactics. One is by refuting the teleological argument (the argument from design). This goes back to Paley's argument that the only sensible and powerful explanation for the marvellous adaptation of the natural world is that it was designed by a loving creator. This argument, as far as it goes, is refuted if evolution occurred as described by Darwin and endorsed by Dawkins. Darwin's theory provides an alternative explanation for the adaptation of the natural world. This is enough for Dawkins to dismiss the 'God' explanation, and any other reasons for asserting the existence of God.

Dawkins also brings up the old problem of evil in a form which is almost a reverse argument from design. In looking at the biological world, Dawkins does not find "all things bright and beautiful" as the old hymn goes. His version is more like the Monty Python satire "all things dull and ugly". The biological world is full of death and suffering—and therefore, Dawkins concludes, could not be the work of a loving creator God. Rather, Dawkins argues that the world more accurately reflects the unconscious, unthinking goal of the survival of DNA. The only thing that life is 'for' is the reproduction of DNA patterns. A loving God would surely not create such a system, in which individuals compete and die simply for their genetic material to survive.

This is a fairly simplistic version of the process of evolution which Dawkins describes more fully in other books, but his purpose here is not merely to explain his 'gene's eye view' understanding of evolution. He specifically wishes to draw theological conclusions from the natural world:

> The universe we observe has precisely the properties we should expect if there is at bottom, no design, no purpose, no evil and no good, nothing but blind, pitiless indifference. As that unhappy poet A. E. Housman put it: For Nature, heartless, witless Nature will neither know nor care. DNA neither knows

nor cares. DNA just is. And we dance to its music.[11]

There is no loving God who is the watchmaker; there is only a blind watchmaker, natural selection, which proceeds without direction or compassion.

Dawkins is not only notoriously harsh on religion, but passionate about his own belief, which he insists is different from religious faith because it is based on evidence. "Faith", he insists, is indeed "one of the world's great evils, comparable to the smallpox virus but harder to eradicate". It is a direct competitor of science—Dawkins has no patience with the idea that religion and science somehow operate on two separate spheres.

> Most religions offer a cosmology and a biology, a theory of life, a theory of origins, and reasons for existence. In doing so, they demonstrate that religion is, in a sense, science; it's just bad science. Don't fall for the argument that religion and science operate on separate dimensions and are concerned with quite separate sorts of questions. Religions have historically always attempted to answer the questions that properly belong to science...They do offer both a cosmology and a biology; however in both cases it is false.[12]

What is most striking about Dawkins' views on science and religion is his persistent belittling of religion and his boosting of science, beyond all scholarly understanding or any traditional views of both those areas. In his view, it is the job of science not just to understand the mechanism by which the world works, but to offer "a theory of life, a theory of origins, and reasons for existence". He admits that science cannot offer

11. Richard Dawkins, *River out of Eden*, *op. cit.*, p. 133.
12. Richard Dawkins, 'Is science a religion?', *The Humanist*, Jan/ Feb 1997, pp. 26-29, p. 27.

"the bereaved a glorious reunion with their loved ones in the hereafter. Those wronged on this earth cannot, on a scientific view, anticipate a sweet comeuppance for their tormentors in a life to come"[13]—as if it were ever within the scope of science to do so. Indeed, his reasoning is constantly of the kind that, since science cannot offer such things, therefore they do not exist. This grants an epistemological sovereignty to science which would astonish most philosophers—not to mention the founders of modern science.

At the same time, Dawkins speaks of the emotional rewards of doing science which he claims surpass any religious feeling.

> Uplift, however, is where science really comes into its own. All the great religions have a place for awe, for ecstatic transport at the wonder and beauty of creation. And it's exactly this feeling of spine-shivering, breath-catching awe—almost worship—this flooding of the chest with ecstatic wonder, that modern science can provide. And it does so beyond the wildest dreams of saints and mystics.[14]

While this passage might reflect Dawkins' ignorance of just how wild the dreams of saints and mystics can be, its most important feature is that it misses the point entirely. Christians feel awe in looking at creation because they know it *is* creation—and they know the creator personally. It is this juxtaposition of images, that the creator who could accomplish so much on such an overwhelming scale would care to concern himself with the most insignificant of humans, that is the inspiration to awe and wonder. Indeed, it is hard to see whence Dawkins derives his glowing joy at contemplating the universe when he also states that "we know from the second

13. *Ibid.*, p. 27.
14. *Ibid.*

law of thermodynamics that all complexity, all life, all laughter, all sorrow, is hell-bent on levelling itself out into cold nothingness in the end. They—and we—can never be more than temporary, local buckings of the great universal slide into the abyss of uniformity".[15] Dawkins' awe of 'creation' is in stark contrast to his actual belief about its origins and destiny. It has in fact been suggested that Dawkins's very sense of the wonder of the universe has been affected by his Christianised upbringing in England's public schools.[16]

Dawkins' vendetta against religion—by which he generally means Protestant Christianity, although he is happy to include all religions under his doctrine of universal rejection—is closely connected with his strong promotion of Darwinian evolution. He protests, as does equally fervent Darwinian Daniel Dennett, that teaching children Christian beliefs is a form of child abuse.[17] It is unusual to find any discussion of evolutionary theory in his writings which does not include, somewhere, a condemnation of creation beliefs. They are not just an alternative to evolutionary theory in his view; they are the *enemy*.

E. O. Wilson: religion subsumed

E. O Wilson, the biologist at the centre of the sociobiology scandal, considers ethics and religion as part of the overall programme of scientific explanation. He believes that the evi-

---

15. *Ibid.*, p. 29.

16. Michael Ruse, comparing Stephen Jay Gould's background with Dawkins's, writes: "Gould did not have the steady diet of natural theology that someone like Dawkins would have had in British schools, especially British private schools. Living in New York...Gould would not have spent his youth collecting butterflies from the meadows, while singing 'All Things Bright and Beautiful' at school assembly. Michael Ruse, *op cit.*, p. 144.

17. Dawkins, 'Is science a religion?', *op. cit.*, p. 28; Daniel C. Dennett, *Darwin's Dangerous Idea: Evolution and the Meanings of Life*, Penguin, London, 1995, p. 516.

dence of biology and the brain sciences favours a purely material origin of ethics.

Wilson grew up a Southern Baptist, and speaks of his experience as a 'reborn evangelical', born again at the age of 15. He rejected that experience later, however, feeling that he had been conned by theatricality.

> When I was 17, I saw that a lot of things that had inspired me earlier were really theatrical staging. And then I had been exposed to evolution, and because I had discovered that what I most loved on the planet, which was life on the planet, made sense only in terms of evolution and the idea of natural selection, and that this was a far more interesting, richer and more powerful explanation than the teachings of the New Testament.[18]

Brought up in a religious atmosphere, probably believing in some sort of literal reading of Genesis, Wilson was overwhelmed by the explanatory power of Darwinism. He still kept, it seems, a respect for religious activity, feeling "by intellect and temperament bound to respect its ancient traditions". But he was determined to demonstrate that his religious upbringing had been, in fact, false. The crucial aspect for him, it seems, was religion's claim to explain ethics. He wished to make "scientific materialism triumph over irrational religious dogma". This, in a way, might characterise the trend of Wilson's entire intellectual career.[19]

The mature theory which Wilson has reached exemplifies this trend. Transcendental religion, he holds, is not true; it is based on a false supernaturalism. However he is not against religion as such; he acknowledges its social and aesthetic

---

18. Personal interview, quoted in Segestrale, *op. cit*, p. 39.
19. See Segestrale, *ibid.*

value, and believes it should be maintained. "It would be a sorry day if we abandoned our venerated sacral traditions", he writes. They are necessary for humanity to be fulfilled.

> People need more than reason. They need the poetry of affirmation, they crave an authority greater than themselves at rites of passage and other moments of high seriousness. A majority desperately wish for the immortality the rituals seem to underwrite…
>
> Whether atheists or true believers, let oaths be taken with hand on the Bible, and may we continue to hear *So help me God*. Call upon priests and ministers and rabbis to bless civil ceremony with prayer, and by all means let us bow our heads in communal respect. Recognize that when introits and invocations prickle the skin we are in the presence of poetry, and the soul of the tribe, something that will outlive the particularities of sectarian belief, and perhaps belief in God itself.[20]

Nonetheless, Wilson believes, the religious systems that produce these rabbis and ministers and priest are based on falsity. The greater authority probably does not exist (although Wilson is humbly agnostic on this point). Even if there is some transcendental reality, there is no deity who can take the responsibility for ethics. What we believe to be right and wrong is entirely up to us. We have evolved to be moral creatures, and our knowledge of morals must come from the natural sciences.

That is, Wilson does not believe in the naturalistic fallacy, that the jump from 'is' to 'ought' is an invalid one. Traditionally this has been a philosophical taboo. It is one thing to describe, by means of natural science or anything else, what is the case. It is a wrong conclusion, philosophers have traditionally held,

---

20. Edward O. Wilson, *Consilience: The Unity of Knowledge*, Abacus, London, 1998, p. 276.

to say that therefore something *ought* to be the case. We may have evolved to be selfish—so what? That doesn't make selfishness right. It doesn't mean we *ought* to be selfish.

This is the line typically taken by Dawkins and other British Darwinians. Wilson, however, rejects it: "For if *ought* is not *is*, what is?". Ethical precepts are not independent truths outside of reality in some Platonic realm or in the mind of God; they are products of the brain and human culture. They are codified behavioural traits which have proved to be useful ones. A moral law is simply the statement of some behavioural principle that humans generally feel strongly about. What we ought to do is simply another way of describing what we *do* do, what we feel strongly about doing and what most people do. Saying 'ought' merely emphasises how strongly we feel about it.

> The individual is seen as predisposed biologically to make certain choices. By cultural evolution some of the choices are hardened into precept, then laws, and if the predisposition or coercion is strong enough, a belief in the command of God or the natural order of the universe. The general empiricist principle takes this form: *Strong innate feeling and historical experience cause certain actions to be preferred; we have experienced them, and weighed their consequences, and agree to conform with codes that express them.*[21]

The way to a better, more ethical society, then, is to take this approach seriously and search for the genetics and environmental history of moral sentiments. When they can be understood and seen for what they are, then our whole ethical structure can be tidied and sorted. At the moment, moral reasoning is a mess, Wilson holds, with old and new ethical precepts mixed together

21. *Ibid.*, p. 279, his italics.

with little order and no understanding. Only when we sort out what is appropriate for our current stage of evolutionary and cultural development can we hope for a moral society.

Similarly, religion can come to be properly understood through natural science. "Religions are analogous to superorganisms. They have a life cycle. They are born, they grow, they compete, they reproduce, and, in the fullness of time, most die." They evolve along with moral reasoning, and are used to justify moral codes, but they are far more than that. "A great subterranean river of the mind, it [the religious drive] gathers strength from a broad spread of tributary emotions." Religion springs from our survival instinct, our wish to understand and control life, and our desire to protect the tribe. Religion has been invented everywhere, and so must be fundamental to our natures: "such inevitability is the mark of instinctual behaviour in any species".[22] In other words, religion exists because it has a hereditary selective advantage; the genes of religious believers are more likely to be passed on than those of iconoclasts who step outside the tribe's belief.

Wilson stresses the need for further research in this area, but asserts that so far the theory that religious behaviour arose from evolution by natural selection fits the data. Just as amongst pack animals there are dominant and subordinate individuals, humans have dominant beings to whom they offer obeisance—religious and civil authority, and ultimately the gods. This is a fruitful survival strategy for wolves and monkeys, and so it makes sense to apply it to humans. We are just more sophisticated in developing our hierarchies. Our flexible "symbol-forming" minds build ritual and prayer, and systems of explanation. We yearn for the ultimate experience of communion,

22. *Ibid.*, pp. 285-287.

which Wilson identifies as the Hindu smadhi, Buddhist Zen stori, Sufi fana, Taoist wu-wei and Pentecostal Christian rebirth. Our brain chemistry creates our religious feeling which is integrated with our instinctual need for pack behaviour.

This leaves us with a great problem—"we evolved genetically to accept one truth and discovered another". What feels most right and is most convincing to us is the existence of the transcendent. What we have discovered to be true, however, Wilson claims, is that there is no such transcendence; we have just evolved to wish there were. There is no way to erase this dilemma, he asserts. There is, however, a way to settle the conflict between the world views.

> The spirits our ancestors knew intimately first fled the ricks and the trees, then the distant mountains. Now they are in the stars, where their final extinction is possible. *But we cannot live without them.* People need a sacred narrative. They must have a sense of larger purpose, in one form or other, however intellectualised....
>
> If the sacred narrative cannot be in the form of a religious cosmology, it will be taken from the material history of the universe and the human species.[23]

Telling the true evolutionary epic, 'retold as poetry', will fulfil this need for sacred narrative. Our new mythos will be based on understanding of our genetic heritage. At the moment, religion still holds the hearts and minds of the majority because its scientific basis has not been fully uncovered; but that will come. "The eventual result of the competition between the two world views, I believe, will be the secularization of the human epic and of religion itself."[24]

23. *Ibid.*, p. 295, his italics.
24. *Ibid.*, p. 296.

Like Dawkins, then, Wilson believes that science can provide mystique and awe the equal of any religion—assuming that a mystical experience is the goal of religion (which is not the case with biblical Christianity). Unlike Dawkins, however, Wilson lacks the sense of fierce antipathy to religion as the enemy of society. On the contrary, Wilson would want to embrace religion as necessary to society and fundamental to being human. He merely wishes to transform it to something true—in his view, evolutionary science. So religion has been tamed, and Wilson's intellectual quest to leave behind his religious upbringing has been fulfilled.

Stephen Jay Gould—two separate worlds

Stephen Jay Gould is another who has been vocal about his views on religion. Like Wilson, he thinks it essential, though without Wilson's evolutionary rationale. For Gould, religion is a magisterium—a domain of thought and teaching—equally valuable with science, and not overlapping with science. At times both science and religion, in Gould's view, have been guilty of treading on each others' turf. When that happens, warfare ensues—not, Gould believes, because there is any essential reason for warfare, but simply because individuals within each magisteria try to claim more authority than is their due. So developing an ethics based on evolutionary theory is as bad as developing a science based on Genesis. Both misunderstand where the domains of science and religion end. But in a true understanding of the appropriate domains for science and religion, Gould feels, all warfare between the two will end.

What Gould defines as 'religion' is extremely broad. It is nothing less than any philosophy of ethics and meaning, with or without a deity, with or without organised doctrine.

Science tries to document the factual character of the natural world, and to develop theories that coordinate and explain these facts. Religion, on the other hand, operates in the equally important, but utterly different, realm of human purposes, meanings, and values—subjects that the factual domain of science might illuminate, but can never resolve. Similarly, while scientists must operate with ethical principles, some specific to their practice, the validity of these principles can never be inferred from the factual discoveries of science.[25]

To solve the problems of science and religion, then, Gould proposes his NOMA principle—Non-Overlapping Magisteria.

...the net, or magisterium, of science covers the empirical realm: what is the universe made of (fact) and why does it work this way (theory). The magisterium of religion extends over questions of ultimate meaning and moral value. These two magisteria do not overlap, nor do they encompass all inquiry (consider, for example, the magisterium of art and the meaning of beauty). To cite the old cliches, science gets the age of rocks, and religion the rock of ages; science studies how the heavens go, religion how to go to heaven.[26]

Gould appears to be sincere in his insistence that the religion magisterium is just as important as science. He admits a fascination with and deep interest in religion, and a rejection of his parents' fierce atheistic Judaism (itself a reaction against their parents' religiosity). While his respect may be genuine, however, he admits himself agnostic—truly not knowing (and not even specifying what it is he does not know). But that does not matter. The importance of the religion magisterium

25. Stephen Jay Gould, *Rocks of Ages: Science and Religion in the Fullness of Life*, The Ballantine Publishing Group, New York, 1999, pp. 4-5.
26. *Ibid.*, p. 6.

is independent of fact, for it does not deal with fact. One can move in the religion magisterium as an atheist or as a devout Catholic. It is about discussion of ethics and what makes life meaningful, not about factual reality.

> Are we worth more than bugs or bacteria because we have evolved a much more complex neurology? Under what conditions (if ever) do we have a right to drive other species to extinction by elimination of their habitats?…These questions address moral issues about the value and meaning of life, both in human form and more widely construed. Their fruitful discussion must proceed under a different magisterium, far older than science (at least as a formalized inquiry), and dedicated to a quest for consensus, or at least a clarification of assumptions and criteria, about ethical 'ought', rather than a search for any factual 'is' about the material construction of the natural world.[27]

Gould, then, presents a schema of science and religion which is a third alternative from Dawkins' rejection and Wilson's acceptance. He does not see religion as an enemy, as Dawkins does; he sees it as a valuable and necessary friend. Neither does he see it subsumed and redefined by science as Wilson does: Gould respects religion as a separate and autonomous domain. However in doing so, he removes from religion any claims to facticity, or even any relevance to that concept. Religion is not something that is true or false. It is something that discusses and ponders.

As far as understanding the problems of moral philosophy, Gould has a fairly strong position, albeit one with a peculiar slant against traditional morality. But he does acknowledge that there are times when the workings and conclusions of one magisterium are very relevant to the other.

27. *Ibid.*, pp. 54-5.

Only the most fearful and parochial moral philosopher would regard such potential scientific information as useless or uninteresting. Such facts can never validate a moral position, but we surely want to understand the sociology of human behaviour, if only to recognize the relative difficulty of instituting various consensuses reached within the magisterium of morals and meaning. To choose a silly example, we had better appreciate the facts of mammalian sexuality, if only to avoid despair if we decide to advocate uncompromising monogamy as the only moral path for human society, and then become confused when our arguments, so forcefully and elegantly crafted, fare so poorly in application.

Similarly, scientists would do well to appreciate the norms of moral discourse, if only to understand why a thoughtful person without expert knowledge about the genetics of heredity might justly challenge an assertion that some particular experiment in the controlled breeding of humans should be done because we now have the technology to proceed, and the results would be interesting within the internal logic of expanding information and explanation.[28]

It might be replied that religion—in particular, Christianity, which is what Gould uses for all his examples—is far more than ethical philosophy. Indeed, without its claims of facticity, its ethics have no basis. Gould tries to remove all claims of fact from Christianity. For his main example, six-day creation science, he has some validity—after all, there are plenty of Christians who are not creation scientists. However, Gould does not mention some of the other far more central Christian claims of fact—that God exists, that the Bible is his word, that Jesus lived on earth and was God incarnate, that he died and rose again. Gould maintains complete respect for

28. *Ibid.*, p. 667.

religion—as long as religion is willing to let go of any such claims to truth. Religion and science can exist harmoniously, but only if religion is no more than moral philosophy, and agnostic moral philosophy at that.

The question remains: Why can we never discuss evolution in a context that does not include religion, in particular attacks on Christianity? One reason is that we probably don't know how to, because it's never been done. Ever since evolutionary theory was first proposed, it has been in some religious context, sometimes pro-religion but more frequently anti-, and that tendency has continued. The Creation Science movement was established out of utter frustration with the illogical attacks made on Christianity, and probably a good deal of its impetus continues to be from evolutionists who make it a particular target.

However, while this may help us understand historically why we have inherited such a close relationship between evolutionary theory and Christianity, it still does not explain why it was there to start with—nor why generations of scholars who might like to discuss the issues independently have never succeeded in changing the public image. It seems that there is something about evolutionary theory that tenaciously hangs onto its religious accretions. Or rather, there is something in us that means we are never quite successful as a race in looking at the theory entirely objectively. To understand the connection between evolutionary theory and religion, we need to dig a little deeper into our understanding of ourselves.

Part IV

UNDERSTANDING OURSELVES

— 16 —

FACTS AND VALUES

It seems to be taken for granted in our scientific society that there are two basic categories of things; one of them we can all agree on, the other one a matter of private difference. So there are facts, and then there are values. There is truth, and then there is opinion. There is rationality and reason, and then there is faith or belief. The 'magisteria' described by Stephen Jay Gould fit very neatly into this way of thinking: science is one thing, but religion something else altogether. The natural world, the real world in which we all live, is something we can all study and come to agree upon. The more fuzzy world of opinion, values, belief, and religion, is a private matter—quite possibly just as important—but not the same sort of thing. It comes quite naturally to us to accept that what is, what actually exists as hard fact, is quite different from what we think ought to be. What is can be tested and experimented on to determine the truth. What ought to be varies from culture to culture and from person to person. It is a very private thing, about one's personal feelings and convictions.

This distinction between fact and value was not so clear-cut in the past. Indeed, in many ways it is the result of Immanuel Kant's philosophising in the eighteenth century. Although it seems quite obvious and fitting in modern, multicultural society, there are many aspects of this division that can be soundly criticised. Yet because we are not used to criticising this distinction—because so much of modern discussion takes it for granted—we are sometimes left in considerable confusion when our instincts seem to go against it. It is this kind of confusion, I believe, that lies at the heart of the intense passion aroused by evolutionary theory. It is not that we can't understand the theory, or that some people are blinded to the facts. There is something more profound going on. Our categories for understanding our own thought processes are simply not suitable for the argument. We are trying to argue about the distinction between science and religion, when the dividing line is actually over something else altogether. It is the line between two different types of religious framework, both of which place particular interpretations upon natural science.

This is where the controversy is: between competing theories of the supernatural world. The science itself operates on a different level: it presents theories of the natural world. Natural science cannot logically draw conclusions about the supernatural. The two are by definition separate areas of study. There might be some clues in the mechanism of how things work, as to whether it was designed or not, but such conclusions are only ever weakly inductive. They are at best hints. It *should* be possible to study the mechanism without any reference to ultimate issues about God (or his absence), or the meaning of life.

Similarly, evolutionary theory just talks about what *is*. It is a logical structure that attempts to bind together disparate bits of evidence into a coherent historical process. Evolution cannot lead to any conclusions about God, about morals or about politics. To do so is to fall into the naturalistic fallacy, which is still a logical fallacy whether or not E. O Wilson chooses to ignore it.

This is the view espoused by many scientists of different religious beliefs, and is the basis of the position generally known as theistic evolution. It insists that the battle between evolution or creation is a false dichotomy; evolution could easily be the *method* of creation. This rests on two assumptions, both logically valid: that not only could God use any method he liked, but any scientific discussion of mechanism implies nothing about the purpose behind it. Because these are logically valid statements, it should be the case that evolutionary science need not comment on ideology at all.

Science, by definition, is a study of the natural world. A scientist simply looks at what is there and describes it, and tries to think of some coherent, physical explanation that would account for it. In principle, evolution need not differ from this idea. If God did choose to have us evolve, then the evidence will be there and there is nothing wrong with someone discovering it. I have enough faith in the integrity of the vast numbers of scientists—Christian and non-Christian—who study the history of life and the universe that they will report the evidence honestly. Surely we can work out whether evolution is true or not on the merits of the theory alone and the evidence for it. Evolution as a theory does not have *necessary* implications for life, God or morality. It need not be associated with these areas at all. It should be the case that evolution is considered purely as a scientific theory. Evolution need not have all these religious connotations.

BUT IT ALWAYS DOES.

It always does. Why?

— 17 —

THE MYTH OF RELIGIOUS NEUTRALITY

Here, the thesis of thousands of commentators about the religious neutrality of science simply does not hold up. Evolution has *always* had a religious framework of some sort. Even as the science of evolution has become more and more rigorous, the standards of prediction and testing more carefully held to, the religious aura in which it operates is as strong as ever. We are no longer in the days of Thomas Huxley who was driven by a political need to promote science regardless of the fact that he disagreed with Darwin's theory. The most vocal advocates of evolutionary theory today are also passionate about the requirements of good science—testing, experimentation, logic and so on. Yet that has not made the theory more scientific and less ideological. The ideology is as strong as ever.

Why? Why is this theory something that we simply cannot divorce from our ideas of meaning and the purpose of life? The answer is not all that surprising—it is because evolutionary theory is *about* life. Indeed, it is about the life with which we are most concerned—our own. When we are talking about human nature, it hits close to home and it *will* mean something to us beyond brute fact. Theories of human origin have always gone along with ideas about the purpose of humanity and our place in the universe. We can't help it. As human beings, whether we are evolved or not, we are living beings who matter. That conclusion is not deriving ought from is; it is a plain statement of the way things are, the way humans have been throughout history. The fact is, there is something special about humans, something which we experience every day as we live, love, mourn, hate, murder, laugh and think. Talking about how humans got here can never be a purely mechanical question, because we simply cannot act as if we are purely mechanisms. Our own lives, our culture, our entire history, demonstrates that.

The nature of human nature

Why do we get so excited about the status of humans? For a simple reason: humans *are* special.

It is true that humans are in the same category as the rest of creation in a physical sense. Science has demonstrated this. We have physiological processes; we have birth and death and procreation; we exist as physical matter just as the rest of nature does. We can be studied scientifically, and scientifically our bodies make sense. We can be dissected and examined and understood as biological, chemical and physical beings.

This is true. Yet there is still much to being human that is distinctly different from the rest of nature. We can't make that difference go away, whatever evolutionary science tells us—even whatever truth evolutionary science tells us. We could have 100% knowledge of our physiological processes, of our chemical structure, and even how that has changed or developed since the beginning of time—and yet there would still be something different about us.

For instance, we may have 97% the same DNA as chimpanzees. The tests to establish this are rigorous and repeatable, and there is no particular reason to doubt them. This is a true statement about humans and chimpanzees. Yet what are we to make of it? We are not chimpanzees, and it is the difference that is the oddity, not the similarity. The 97% similarity merely makes it even more astonishing that humans are as different as they are. What is it about us that makes us special?

Why are we concerned with justice, love, linguistics, communication and society? What could make a 97%-chimpanzee being like this? The 97% similarity does not prove that we are 'just' apes. It proves that there is something very strange about being human.

The very fact that evolutionary science concerning humans always provokes loud cries on all fronts shows that there is something there to be upset about. Creationists did not create the controversy over evolutionary theory. It was always there because no-one has a theory of human origins without a theory of what humanity is. Evolutionary theory always contained a theory of what humanity is—whether organisms who evolved by chance, who are not above the animals and not in the image of God; or organisms who have developed in an inevitable progression towards higher beings; or organisms created by God in a slow but guided process. As we have seen this still continues, as many evolutionary theorists are driven in their theorising by their conviction of what humanity is, not the other way around. We are not, and (it seems) *cannot*, be detached and objective about our origins. They do mean something to us, and this is not just the remnant of religious sentiment. It's still there in the most fierce anti-religious apologists of evolution.

However, these same anti-religious apologists try to insist that evolution is only about science. Well, it is polemically convenient for atheists if evolutionary theory is believed to be purely scientific and neutral. Then when they claim that evolution disproves Christianity they can present this as a conclusion based on science. It is not; it is a conclusion based on ideology, in fact a conclusion drawn before evolutionary theory was formulated at all. Evolutionary theory, in itself, never was a scientific theory which challenged the prevailing theory of God's creation. It was a use of scientific ideas to attack God's creation. It was always ideological, and still is.

But there is another, deeper issue here. Even if a scientific theory of human origins and nature had not been developed in an anti-Christian atmosphere, it is highly unlikely it would ever have been neutral. Although we keep on trying to be neutral about such theories, it seems we just can't do it. We have been told the traditional story that Copernicus moved us from the centre of the universe, Darwin removed us from the peak of creation, and Freud removed us from the throne of self-control and rationality. This is not only a historic distortion, it just didn't work. We won't be dethroned, no matter how hard we try. We keep falling across the awkward fact that we *are* more than animals. The question is not whether we are different, but how we deal with the undeniable difference that exists.

Atheists have to cope with the reality of human difference. The most common tactic is simply to deny difference. But that is to deny reality. This is logically consistent with evolutionary science, but it contradicts daily lived human experience.

For without God, it is impossible rationally to maintain the 'specialness' of humans. This is the real issue: not whether evolution is true or not, but whether or not we are created. If not, then we are meaningless accidents. We have no particular basis for culture, aesthetics, communication or faith in our own powers of reason. Postmodern scholarship has recognised this to some extent, and it is fiercely rejected by most sciences. Yet you can't have it both ways. If we are just animals, we are not special.

This is the hole that a purely materialistic science has dug for itself—it finds itself unable to explain being human as we experience it. Accordingly, this is essentially why any discussion of origins, whether theist or atheist or any position in between, ends up combining ideology with science.

Wilson does it by including religion in his science; that religion, since it is so pervasive, is obviously an adaptation and so we should keep it. But the content of traditional religion is clearly wrong, so he replaces it with reverence for evolution and the natural world. Dawkins and others, even though they insist they are doing away with religion, essentially do the same thing; they fill their science with religious imagery in an attempt to satisfy religious feeling with awe of science.

The point that atheist evolutionists refuse to face is that without a creator, human life makes no sense. When atheists take science beyond its scope, and claim the explanation of mechanisms to be a complete and sufficient explanation for all of reality, their science becomes a failure on its own terms. For to be successful, a scientific theory must adequately explain the reality it is addressing. Evolution, when placed within a purely materialist or atheist framework, strikingly fails at this point. It does not explain humanity.

⊷18⊷

A FAILURE TO EXPLAIN

How is it that we are animals, but that we don't live like animals? Why is it so necessary to find a way to deal with religion within evolutionary debate, even if you don't believe in it? Why do we seem to need morality and meaning?

As we have seen, various explanations have been offered. We are just self-deluding; we think we're important, when we're actually not. Or religion is a necessary survival strategy, even though it doesn't mean anything. Or it's innate and meaningful, even though we don't really understand how that can be in this physical universe.

A far better explanation for our odd situation, of being both so similar to animals and yet so different, is that there really is a God who has created humans and has a special relationship with them. We are not just evolved machines. Our sense of personhood, our feelings of purpose, our desire for love and goodness, are not delusions. So much about being human seems to indicate that we're special because, in fact, we *are* special.

Ever since the enlightenment, Western intellectuals have been trying to make sense of being human without recognising God. Finally we can start to see how badly that project has failed. The fact is, we *don't* make sense without God. There *is* morality and nobility and literature and art and love and meaning. That these things exist is, in a real sense, quite miraculous. Evolutionary theory as it stands in its most detailed glory demands the miraculous, because it cries out for an explanation of how evolved apes could become people.

Yet if there is no God—if there is only matter, acted upon

by blind, chance forces—there is no justification for saying that humans matter. We can have no ultimate justification for morality, responsibility or worth. Yet we cannot let these things go and still live. So the atheist, the materialist, grasps hold of these things but denies the God who makes them possible. It is an irrational position to be in. It is, ultimately, an impossible position. Rarely do atheists acknowledge this. They write passionately about the satisfaction to be found in the idea of evolution, as if that makes it better. It is too difficult to face the reality that without God, humans don't really matter.

The problem is not evolution versus creation. It is not even science versus religion. *It is materialism versus reality.* We are being misled by atheistic evolutionists, who have a religious conviction that clashes with their science. Even if it's an entirely negative religious conviction that insists humans are nothing more than animals, this conviction clashes with the observed facts of living. You can deny the difference of humans or attempt to explain it away, but we all know that it's there.

What does this mean for understanding evolutionary theory? We need to acknowledge that the truly significant thing about evolutionary theory is not the theory itself, but the framework in which it is held. Controversy arises because we are trying to explain ourselves to ourselves. The mechanism is not really important; what we are passionate about is the meaning of being human. That is something which people essentially decide on ideological grounds, and science is made to fit in with it.

Evolutionary theory does not, of course, prove that there is no creator God. But evolutionary theory held by a theist is a completely different theory of origins from evolutionary theory held by an atheist. One is telling the details of how a loving Father created us to be fully human and capable of becoming his children. The other is telling the details of how a bizarre accident incidentally brought about a meaningless set of intelligent apes. We must recognise these theories for what they are. The atheist theory is no more scientific than the theist one, and the truth of either will not be established on facts of the fossil record or genetic populations. The best way to approach the question of which is true is to consider which best explains reality. Are we truly people, with ideas that matter and lives that mean something? Or are we just apes, with delusions of grandeur?

⊷ 19 ⊷
SOME CONCLUSIONS

We have covered a lot of ground in this book, to gain a perspective on Darwinism. We have seen that the theory itself has changed and developed since Darwin's day, and that the modern evolutionary theory incorporates a vast range of new ideas quite foreign to Darwin himself—so, in fact, to call evolutionary theory 'Darwinian' these days is more of an historical note than a true description.

We have also canvassed some of the controversies within the world of modern evolutionary biology. Some of the debates are loud and public, some heard only within scientific circles. We have seen some of the depth of disagreement between working scientists on different aspects of evolutionary theory.

We have also seen that, as far as religion is concerned, evolutionary theory has never been neutral. Since its actual invention as a scientific theory, it has been presented with specific religious connotations. Evolutionary theory has always been more than 'just' a scientific theory. It has always been, quite overtly and deliberately, a tool of political propaganda—most often anti-Christian propaganda.

Is evolution true?

So what is the truth of the matter? Is evolution true, or is it not? Did our physical bodies, so similar in so many ways to apes, actually descend from a common ancestor with the apes? The answer would be that, at present, it's hard to say. It is possible. There is evidence of development and adaptation in the genetic structure of organisms, and in the fossil record of past organisms. Yet many questions remain, and there is a lot of data which is still effectively unexplained—or explained in a multitude of conflicting ways. The fossil record doesn't quite fit everybody's theories. The structure of the cell is more complicated than expected. In many areas, the details of evolution are left blank.

We may never know every detail of the matter, for we will always be limited to piecing together a probable theory from limited data. The historical processes which have occurred in our physical development are in the past, and we cannot go back to witness for ourselves what exactly happened.

Yet we need not be defeatist. As humans, we do have the ability to study our world and come to likely conclusions, and we may well discover the answer. In the end, whether or not evolutionary theory is true, or the most probable theory, will become obvious as it confronts the data. If it is a true account of the development of life, then it will continue to have experimental triumphs and to increase in explanatory power. Many of its problems will be overcome and current anomalies explained.

If it is, on the other hand, a theory which is driven by ideology and ignores relevant facts, then it will be shown up as such eventually. Even if it takes centuries, truth about the world can not be suppressed forever. It may well be that evolutionary theory will be superseded by some other theory, as these anomalies mount up and the theory crumples under the weight of evidence. Most scientists follow where the evidence takes them. The practice of science may have its flaws, and the scientific community may have its charlatans and its blind ideologues, but if the evidence is there it will be recognised sooner or later. A significantly different theory about the development of life, which unites all the known data and explains previous anomalies, would be an exciting thing. It could develop. Science is like that.

Does it really matter?

Maybe in twenty years' time, or fifty, or next century, we will have a better scientific theory of the development of life on earth. Perhaps there is some new discovery to be made in biology, or physics, or mathematics, or paleontology, which will inspire a whole new approach and a new scientific discipline. This is the way empirical science works. Theories are constantly proposed, tested, modified, tested, and modified again. Almost by definition, science never arrives at an absolute and final answer—only at a theory or explanation which best fits the facts as we currently know them.

This is why it is foolish to modify our views on non-scientific questions—such as the meaning of life, or the nature of humanity, or the truth of God—in order to bring them into line with current scientific theories. Almost as soon as we do so, science moves on and declares that particular theory to be no longer adequate.

We need to realise that if evolutionary theory is discarded because of new discoveries or the accumulation of contrary evidence, it will be the theory that crumples, not the ideology. A scientist who is an atheist and holds to evolutionary theory is just as capable of being an atheist and holding to post-evolutionary theory. Even if the post-evolutionary theory is of the appearance of life over six twenty-four hour days, six thousand years ago, there will be those who hold this theory in an atheistic framework if that is their conviction. The theory is a matter of mechanical details. The framework determines its importance.

What we need to be debating, then, is the framework, not the theory. Arguing about evolutionary 'facts' will not accomplish much—unless you are an evolutionary biologist and it is your job to do so. The really important ideas, the ideas that affect our lives and our world, are not based on experimental results, but on a view of reality. That is where we should concentrate our attention. That is where the real truth is to be found.

Thus, a second answer to the question of whether evolutionary theory is true is this: *it doesn't really matter*. Some physical process was involved in bringing us to our current biological state. Whatever process it was, if you know God then you know that he guided that process. However, that will not necessarily tell you much about the process, for God has left us free to discover what mechanisms he has chosen to use in this wonderful creation of his, and some of his mechanisms have been breathtakingly surprising. We cannot say *a priori* that God made his creation work in this way or that way. It may seem bizarre, even uncomfortable, to us that God developed humans from apes. What of it? Other people find it uncomfortable that God might have created humans instantaneously with no intermediate steps. What we find uncomfortable or not is hardly the issue. We do not and cannot dictate how God has worked.

The founders of modern science understood this, in the seventeenth century. Indeed it was this conviction that largely drove science—the conviction that we cannot know how God has worked (and continues to work) in his world unless we go and look. We cannot sit at home and deduce from first principles, or even from the Bible, how God put his commands into practice. God is free. He has, graciously, told us a great deal about himself and his plans, particularly his plans about salvation. But he has been fairly sparse on the physical details.

God remains in control, even of processes which look chaotic and random to us. Look at political history, for instance. On the surface, an atheist could study Israel's history and see the rise and fall of kings, and political manoeuvres within the ancient world, without understanding any of God's hand in it. One could look at Assyria's conquering of Israel and explain it in terms of Assyria's greater military strength—and that explanation would be true. What an outside observer would not understand, of course, is that God gave Assyria the greater military strength so as to punish Israel. From the outside, only God's mechanism can be observed. It takes God's revelation to understand the real importance of what happened. The mechanism could have been anything—Assyria, Babylon, Egypt, a plague—that is purely a matter of historical detail. The really important explanation has to do with God's purposes.

If God used evolution to bring humans to their current physical status, then he did. It does not make any of his revelation about humans less true; and if we do not understand how that revelation relates to particular mechanistic details, then that is hardly important. Whatever mechanism God used, he still created humans, and it is not for us to complain about the mechanism. Of course, we have every right to complain about other humans insisting that some particular mechanism excludes God's action. That is simply nonsense. But God is free to act in his world, and we cannot say in advance exactly how he has done so.

Let me repeat. Is evolution true? *It's hard to say, and it doesn't really matter.*

If what you are really concerned about is the existence of God, or the truth of the Bible, then you can know that these are true on the basis of Jesus' real historical presence and teaching, on the true history of Israel in the Old Testament, or because of the absolute truthfulness of the Bible's descriptions of life and human nature. There are plenty of ways in which you might become convinced that the Bible is true.

If you care about what is special about humans, what makes us different and what our responsibilities are to the world and before God, then the Bible is the place to look. Evolutionary theory, whether true or not, is simply an interesting detail in the story of a greater and far more important truth: that this is God's world.

WHAT ABOUT GENESIS?

There will no doubt be many who have read up to this point thinking to themselves, "Yes, yes, but was there an historical Adam? Which side is she going to come down on? Is Genesis 1-3 true or not?"

This is a fair question in light of all that has been said. The argument so far has essentially been that Darwinism, rightly understood, makes very little difference to our understanding of Christianity. It is one current theory (or set of competing theories) about how certain things happened in our world; but I have argued that it has been the *ideological framework* in which this science has been placed that has been antagonistic to Christianity—not the science itself. The science itself is quite irrelevant to Christian belief and practice. God could have done things one way; or he could have done it another. Whether he created everything very quickly, or very slowly, or using a combination of both, says nothing about whether he was behind the process, and what his purposes were in doing so.

However, there is one circumstance under which even the science itself would be hostile to Christianity—and that is if it made God out to be a liar. If, in the Bible, God proposed an entirely different mechanism for how the world came to be, and claimed that this was the nature of reality, then we would have a problem. If what was asserted in the Bible was flatly contradicted by the weight of evidence accumulated by science, then we would have a real challenge to Christian belief.

For example, if God proclaimed in the Bible that the world was in fact supported upon a giant tortoise, and described the size, weight, age and nature of the tortoise, how it got there, and what it was for, then that would present a real problem for believing in the truthfulness of God—for we have no evidence that the world is supported by a giant tortoise, and whatever evidence we do have points away from such a suggestion.

The real question now becomes apparent. Is Genesis 1-3 to be read as an alternative explanation of the mechanism by which God created the world, or does it make no claims in this area? Is it asserting some basic historical facts—such as that the entire world and everything that inhabits it was created in 144 hours, and that this happened between 6000 and 10000 years ago—or is this not a good reading of the text?

This is something over which Christians have differed in recent times. On the whole, the difference has been not so much about whether the Genesis account is true, but over how much it is saying.

In other words, the issue has been about how we read the Bible. And the answer is: *much like any other book.*

Why we must read the Bible literally[1]

People often ask, 'Do you believe the Bible is true?'. They then ask a further question: 'But do you believe it is literally true?'. The problem is, it is often unclear what the difference is between the two questions. The word 'literally' is thrown around a lot, and often used as a criticism: 'If you don't believe it's literally true then you don't really believe it'. The difficulty is in working out what 'literally' means; it is often used either ambiguously or applied inappropriately.

It may be stating the obvious, but the Bible is a book, or rather a collection of 66 books. It contains poetry, historical narratives, psalms, drama, laws, prophecies, letters, proverbs, love songs and other literary forms. In other words, the Bible is a library of different kinds of literature, and in order to understand it, we must read it on its own terms. If we're reading a

1 This section is adapted from material in my earlier work, *Unnatural Enemies*, Sydney, Matthias Media, 1997, pp. 57-9.

part of the Bible which is poetic in form, we shouldn't read it in the same way as we would an historical narrative—any more than we would read a road directory in order to find a phone number. A piece of writing needs to be read on its own terms, as it presents itself to us. This is what it means to read something 'literally'—to seek the author's intent or content through the literary vehicle by which he chooses to express himself.

Perhaps a brief example may illustrate the point. Psalm 19 says that God has set up a tent in the heavens for the sun, who emerges like a bridegroom from his wedding canopy and runs his course across the sky like a strong athlete—and this expresses the glory and wonder of God's creation. As we read this, we know immediately that the author is not making some kind of mechanistic description of a giant tarpaulin that God has somehow erected in the sky. Nor is he suggesting that the sun has legs. Nor is he making a scientific assertion that the sun moves while the earth stands still. To derive information of that kind from the psalm, or to suggest that the psalmist was even addressing these matters, is to do terrible violence to the psalm as a piece of writing. More than that, it's to do terrible violence to the practice of reading and comprehension, which is one of humanity's greatest achievements. The author of Psalm 19 is simply using the very normal techniques of poetry and imagery to make his point, the kind of imagery we use every day when we speak of 'sunrise', even though we now know that the sun does not 'rise' at all, but is stationary in relation to the earth. To not recognise this is a failure to read what is there.

What would it mean, then, to read Psalm 19 'literally'? We would learn, among other things, that the daily path of the sun is a grand and majestic thing that expresses God's glory and greatness. Moreover, the poetic picture the author draws helps us appreciate what he means; it actually conveys some of that grandeur and strength in a way that a very plain description would not. However, if we were to suggest that the author was really trying to tell us that there was a tent up there, and that the sun had legs, that would not be reading literally at all. It would be against the literal sense of the text, since it is clearly poetic in form, and demands to be read that way.

All reading involves understanding the kind of thing we're reading (the 'genre'), and adjusting our perceptions and reading style accordingly. We do this quite automatically in our daily lives, as we read a newspaper editorial, a cartoon, a letter from a friend or a glossy magazine ad. It seems, however, that people often leave these everyday skills behind when they approach the Bible.

Reading Genesis literally

For a moment, then, let us leave Darwinism to one side and read Genesis on its own terms, as it presents itself to us. Let us try to put aside all the questions and controversies, and do what we should do with any piece of writing—just read it, listening to what the author is saying through the particular form of writing he is using.

As we read Genesis 1, for example, what do we learn by looking at the text? What sort of writing is this? Is it a historical narrative describing the factual details of certain events that took place? Or is it more stylised and poetic in form?

The first thing we notice is that the writing is carefully structured and organized. The account of the creation of the world unfolds in a pattern, with a regular repetition of words and phrases. At each stage of the creation, we read:

> And God said, Let there be... and there was... And God saw that it was good... and there was evening and there was morning ... day.

It is highly stylised, and uses a number of literary devices to convey the fact that God created the world in an effortless, orderly and rational way. By the end of the chapter, the chaos and emptiness of verses 1-2 has been replaced with an orderly and beautifully designed creation that is 'very good'.

The style of writing is not quite like poetry—we don't find the conventions of rhyme, rhythm and imagery that we would normally expect in Hebrew poetry. But neither is the writing like historical narrative, where we would expect more concrete details of time and place, and where the prose would be more flowing in its narration rather than so carefully structured. The exalted and carefully crafted language of Genesis 1 is almost like a hymn or overture. In fact, the chapter functions as a kind of overture to the rest of the book of Genesis.

The literary character of Genesis 1 might suggest to us that it is not written as a strictly chronological reporting of events. The actual content of the material only confirms this impression. For example, light is created on day one, yet the sun and moon are created "to give light upon the earth" on day four. Their function is to separate day from night, and thus to create the framework "for days and years". And yet we have already had three "days" go by in the structure of the account.

The non-chronological nature of Genesis 1:1-2:3 is further seen in Genesis 2:4, where the account starts out with a different timeframe, describing in detail the creation of one man and his wife. This takes place "in *the day* that the LORD God made the earth and the heavens".[2] Clearly "day" in this verse means something other than a 24-hour period of time; it

---

2 See KJV, RV, RSV, NRSV, ESV, NASB. The NIV translates 'in the day' as simply 'when', which is defensible as a translation, but not entirely helpful given the importance of the word 'day' in chapter 1.

means something like 'the general time at which', a fact which adds to our impression that chapter 1 may not be setting out to describe a strictly chronological period of 144 hours.

This verse in 2:4 is the beginning of the real narrative of the book, telling the story of how Adam's race rebelled against God, what the disastrous consequences were, and how God acted to begin to redeem the situation through one particular family line of Adam's. Interestingly, this narrative describes the order of creation differently from chapter 1, with the man being formed first and then the animals.[3]

It is also worth noticing that Genesis 2-3 (and following) does not seem to be an exhaustive account of everything that happened. Who, for example, was Cain afraid of being killed by in chapter 4? And whom did he marry? And why did Cain build a city in Genesis 4:17 if there was only himself, his wife and his son to live in it?

In other words, putting these things together, it would seem to be poor reading to claim that Genesis 1-2 is making particular scientific-style claims about the time-frame and exact mechanistic detail by which God created the world and humanity. Old Testament scholar G. J. Wenham puts it like this:

> The Bible-versus-science debate has, most regrettably, sidetracked readers of Gen 1. Instead of reading the chapter as a triumphant affirmation of the power and wisdom of God and the wonder of his creation, we have been too often bogged down in attempting to squeeze Scripture into the mold of the latest scientific hypothesis or distorting scientific facts to fit a particular interpretation. When allowed to speak for itself, Gen 1 looks beyond such minutiae. Its proclamation of the God of grace and power who undergirds the

---

3   Again, see the KJV, RV, RSV, NRSV, ESV and NASB translation of Gen 2:19.

world and gives it purpose justifies the scientific approach to nature. Gen 1, by further affirming the unique status of man, his place in the divine program, and God's care for him, gives a hope to mankind that atheistic philosophies can never legitimately supply.[4]

From Genesis 1-3 we learn much about the human condition, and the way the world is. We learn why humans are creatures, but at the same time different from all other creatures, and responsible for looking after them. We learn that humans are capable of fellowship with God, and yet are rebellious against him. We learn that the created order is good, and yet also now flawed.

What is so striking about the early chapters of Genesis when we actually read them is not how contradictory they are to the modern world, but how stunningly true they are to the world as we experience it.

What really matters

So is evolution true? As I have already suggested, if by 'evolution' we mean the range of current theories that attempts to explain the process whereby life on earth developed, the answer is: it's hard to say. Evolutionary theory has been through so much change, and is subject to such fierce internal disputes, that it is not unreasonable to imagine the theory completely collapsing at some stage in the future. Of course, it may not. There is much that is persuasive about some aspects of evolutionary theory. But there is also much that is unconvincing and contradictory.

My point is that whether the theory does collapse or not is

4 G. J. Wenham, *Word Biblical Commentary: Genesis 1-15*, Word, 1987, p. 40.

largely irrelevant. The exact description of how we got here doesn't really matter. It's a technical detail. The really important questions that face us, both individually and corporately, will not be solved by continued research into the mechanistic details of how life on earth developed. Questions like: Who are we, as humans? Does life have meaning and purpose? Is there such a thing as truth and justice? How should we relate to one another and the environment? Why do we make art, and what makes good art? What is the best way to live and enjoy life?

If we are meaningless evolved matter, as the atheistic evolutionists contend, these questions are not only insoluble; they are by definition meaningless. A purely materialist view of the world, in which the mechanism is all that exists, cannot provide any satisfactory answers to these questions—nor should it try to do so. And as I have already argued, it cannot even account for or explain the existence of these questions, and their abiding interest for us. It cannot explain humanity, and the fact of our uniqueness.

In other words, it utterly fails to do everything that Genesis 1-3, and the rest of the Bible, does so successfully—to provide a cogent explanation for the way the world is, the way we are, and how we are to relate to another, and to God our Creator.

The theory of evolution cannot keep people from God, as the many scientifically trained people who have nonetheless accepted the saving grace of Christ testifies. If an evolutionist is against God, changing his theory of mechanism will not change his mind about God. This is true in practice, and the practice reflects the place we should give evolutionary theory in our thinking. Evolution is not an explanation of the world which challenges the biblical explanation of the world. It is an attempt at a mechanistic explanation, which may or may not be the process that God used in his creation of the world.

If we understand this fully, we will see that the competition is not between explanation by God and explanation by evolution; it is between an explanation that tells us something vital and interesting, and one that doesn't. It's between an explanation that really explains us and our world, and gives meaning and understanding, and one that quarrels over the details of the mechanism. Both may be true, but only one is really important.

If evolutionary theory (whatever becomes of it) describes a physical process that truly happened, then we have learned something about the natural world, and that is a good thing. But we have not learned anything about who we really are as people. We have not learned anything particularly special about God, for we already knew that he uses physical processes when he wants to. We have not learned how to relate to God or how to understand our own perceptions of value and morality and evil. Even if what evolutionary theory tells us is true, it does not tell us what is really important.

Unless you are a biologist, then, what you believe about the current state of evolutionary theory is not of very great consequence. It won't impinge upon your daily life. After all, consider your attitudes towards other scientific theories. Do you believe in super-string theory? Do you think the P300 trace in EEGs is a valid indicator of cognitive status? Do you believe *Phythophthora infestans* was responsible for the Irish potato famine? You probably have no opinion whatsoever on these things—or even much idea what they're talking about—and it really doesn't matter outside the specialist fields in which these questions are currently being studied.

But whether you obey God or not—now that is important. That matters every day, to everyone, and will matter for all eternity. Understanding what God says is a topic that is important to everyone, and should be interesting to everyone. It sheds light on what matters most to us as humans: how to relate to each other, why we act the way we do, how we should bring up children, and how we should understand love and hate and good and evil.

Whether or not God made the world is therefore a crucially important question. It's a subject to be passionate about. Evolutionist or non-evolutionist, biologist or garden-weeder, it concerns us all.

Other Matthias Media resources from the same author...

kategoria: a critical review
Quarterly Journal

As Christians in a non-Christian world, we are used to apologetics—that is, defending the faith from the attacks. *kategoria* is the other side of apologetics. It is 'speaking against'; going on the offensive. It is asking the questions, querying the suppositions, and critiquing the philosophies and ideas that pervade our modern world, unchallenged.

kategoria is a quarterly journal of quality Christian research which aims to question and uncover the false thinking and unfounded conclusions of the non-Christian world. It is designed to arm the thinking Christian with information to relate to the non-Christian world. In particular, it will be valuable for:

- preachers looking for material to fortify their congregations;
- academics and tertiary students interested in a Christian critique of their field;
- Christian teachers and journalists trying to integrate their convictions into their role as society's gatekeepers;
- anyone who is prepared to put some Christian thought into their world.

Editor: Dr Kirsten Birkett

FOR MORE DETAILED SUBSCRIPTION INFORMATION CONTACT:

Australia

Matthias Media
Telephone: +61-2-9663 1478
Facsimile: +61 2-9663 3256
Email: sales@matthiasmedia.com.au

United Kingdom

The Good Book Company
Telephone: +20-8942 0880
Facsimile: +20-8942-0990
Email: admin@thegoodbook.co.uk

www.matthiasmedia.com.au